MAN AND SPACE

BY

CLIVE E. DAVIS

ILLUSTRATED WITH PHOTOGRAPHS

DODD, MEAD & COMPANY   NEW YORK   1960

Books by Clive E. Davis

THE JUNIOR AIRMAN'S BOOK OF AIRPLANES

THE BOOK OF MISSILES

MAN AND SPACE

The jacket picture of MAN AND SPACE presents space travel of the not-too-distant future as pictured in an artist's concept, painted by W. C. House, Director Systems Management at Azusa, California, where studies of Moon rockets and exotic propulsion methods are expected to furnish the means of propulsion for tomorrow's outer space vehicles. The painting depicts both graphically and realistically the approach of a nuclear propelled space rocket to a satellite station 3,000 miles above the western part of the United States and Central America, at approximately 4:20 P.M., on March 20. The rocket en route to Mars after its satellite stop, is seen at 120 degrees west longitude and 15 degrees north latitude. In addition to being an expert engineer, Mr. House is a skilled aircraft pilot and an unusually capable artist. Photo courtesy of Aerojet-General Corporation.

Library of Congress Catalog Card Number: 60-9594
Printed in the United States of America

CONTENTS

PREFACE   4

1 — WHAT WE KNOW ABOUT SPACE   5

2 — WHAT WE KNOW ABOUT THE EARTH   15

3 — THE MILITARY IN SPACE   20

4 — MAN INTO SPACE   26

5 — PROBING SPACE   61

6 — SUMMARY OF THE UNITED STATES SPACE PROGRAM   74

7 — YOU AND SPACE   81

8 — ORBITAL FLIGHT PATHS   90

GLOSSARY   92

INDEX   94

PREFACE

The American taxpayer often finds occasion to question the necessity for the fantastic expenditures connected with our attempts to conquer space. Because the urgency of our military requirements has been the prime motivation for the development of missiles and space-probing devices, we are apt to overlook the by-products of this effort. The test of time may prove these by-products to be more significant than the original objective.

Obstacles to progress exist primarily in the minds of men. With the acquisition of knowledge, these barriers become understandable and vulnerable to new methods of conquest. Our advance into space has already created new fields of endeavor, has elevated previously secondary sciences into major professions and has produced totally new sciences. This trend has not only opened up many new fields of career opportunities, it has also placed an increased demand upon our educational system to produce the adequately trained men and women who will become the essential and deciding factor in the conquest of space and the preservation of the advances we make.

The purpose of this small book is to consider not only the potential military utilization of space but also the multiplicity of benefits to mankind, all of a peaceful nature, which will inevitably accrue from our efforts in the total space program.

My sincere thanks go to the many representatives of industry and their companies; to the individuals and agencies of the United States Government and the Armed Forces, for the assistance given me in collecting and compiling the material presented. Special thanks to my friend, John F. Loosbrock, editor of *Air Force,* the Magazine of Aerospace Power, for the use of the excellent charts and diagrams from that publication. The text contains many comments which are those of the author and do not necessarily represent the opinions of those who cooperated in this effort.

CLIVE E. DAVIS

Sacramento, California.

1/WHAT WE KNOW ABOUT SPACE

Man has always had a lively curiosity about space. As soon as the ancient caveman learned how to make impressions upon a rock, he decorated his walls with crude stars, moons and suns. From the beginning of recorded history we know men have gazed into the heavens, wondered about what they saw and tried to draw conclusions from their observations.

Astronomy, the scientific study of the celestial bodies and their movements, is probably the oldest of all sciences. The ancient Greeks seem to have been the first important astronomers. Though none of them ever achieved any great degree of individual recognition, their thoughts and observations were the basis for theories developed years later by other men. Ptolemy, the first renowned astronomer, born in Egypt in 100 A.D., based his theories of the universe on the ideas of the ancient Greek, Hipparchus.

Time was to prove that Ptolemy picked the wrong Greek as his guide but he was to gain great fame through his writings on the universe. He advanced the theory that the Earth was the center of the universe, that it was a stationary globe around which revolved the sphere of the heavens with forty-eight constellations and seven planets, including the Moon, Mercury, Venus, Mars, Jupiter, Saturn and the Sun. He explained the mathematical arrangement of the stars and made calculations on the positions of the planets. Ptolemy's most ambitious writing was a thirteen-volume work he called, *The Almagest*. That is an Arabic word meaning "the greatest construction." In this work, Ptolemy went into lengthy explanations of his theories, derived chiefly from the recorded thoughts of Hipparchus who is thought to have died about 125 B.C.

Because of his voluminous and convincing writing, Ptolemy was able to impress his Ptolemaic system so thoroughly upon the world that for the fantastic period of about 1400 years no one questioned its accuracy. For that unbelievable length of time in the development of knowledge man's continuing efforts to solve the secrets of the universe were based upon an incorrect theory. The circumstances under which the Ptolemaic system was finally proved false are almost as unbelievable.

Nicholaus Copernicus was born in Thorn, Prussian Poland, in the year 1473. He studied astronomy and mathematics at the University of Cracow, then took up Greek and philosophy for three years at the

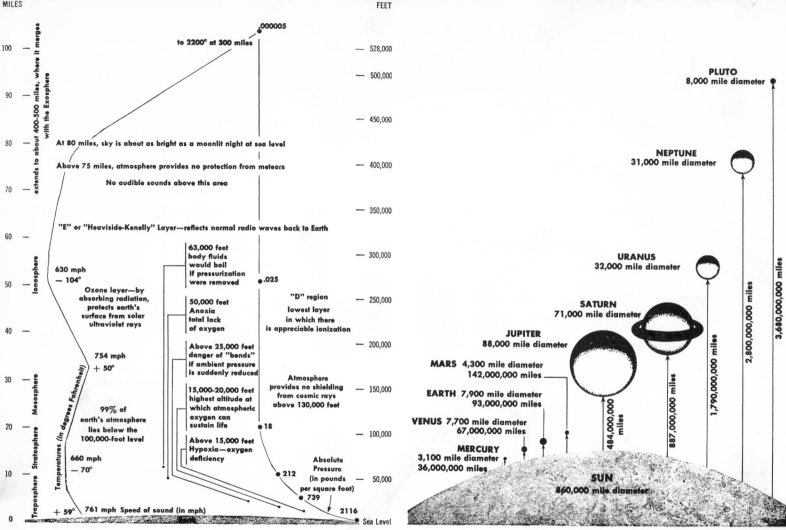

THE HAZARDS OF SPACE Chart above illustrates the dangers to man as he rises up and out of the Earth's atmosphere. From 15,000-20,000 feet is the highest altitude where atmospheric oxygen will sustain life. At 63,000 feet, blood boils. At 80,000 feet, a sealed cabin with self-contained environment is mandatory. At 130,000 feet, atmospheric shielding of cosmic rays ends. Ninety-nine percent of the atmosphere is located below the 100,000-foot level. Physiological "space equivalence" begins far below that. Above 75 miles, atmospheric shielding against meteors ends.

VAST DISTANCES OF OUR SOLAR SYSTEM and the diameters of its nine planets are illustrated her To a Plutonian, more than 3,680,000,000 miles away, the sun would look like not much more than a star, while a Mercurian, "only" 36,000,000 miles away, the sun would appear as a huge fiery orb in the heavens. Of all the planet Earth seems to be ideally situated, just far enough away from the sun (93,000,000 miles) to provide balanced and con fortable temperatures, radiation, and light ranges to nurture the life that has developed on this planet over the age

University of Bologna, in Italy. After that, he decided upon a career in the Catholic Church and continued his studies at the University of Ferrara, receiving a doctor's degree in canon law in 1503. He was made a canon at the Cathedral of Frauenberg, East Prussia, and held that position until his death in 1543. Throughout his entire life, his main hobby was astronomy.

Perhaps because of his Greek studies, Copernicus, like Ptolemy, became interested in the ideas of the early Greek astronomers. The more he delved into them, the more he became convinced that the Ptolemaic system was not correct and that the Earth was not the center of the universe. He often expressed these sentiments to his friends and, upon their insistence, he eventually wrote a manscript titled, *Concerning the Revolutions of the Celestial Spheres*, which he dedicated to Pope Paul III. In this work, Copernicus set forth his theory that the Sun is the center of the planets, a theory that is the basis for our modern astronomy.

However, Copernicus felt some of his notions about the movements of the Earth and the planets might be in conflict with the teachings of the Church, so for thirty-six years he kept his manuscript hidden and would not allow it to be published. Again, close friends prevailed upon him, and he finally consented to the publication. He died a few hours after receiving a copy of his work and he never knew that he had achieved lasting fame as the father of modern astronomy.

While Copernicus was concerning himself with the development of a new theory of astronomy, other men were using the positions of the Sun, the Moon, planets and stars to develop a means of finding their way from one place to another. This was the beginning of the science of celestial navigation, used in the time of Copernicus by Christopher Columbus in discovering America, and through the centuries which have followed by all ships that sail the seas. The very same system is used today by navigators in the Strategic Air Command's B-52 jet bombers.

Since the time of Copernicus, the science of astronomy has steadily added to our fund of information about the celestial bodies and their movements through space. Russian lunar rockets and satellites have dramatically demonstrated how accurate this data is.

When the Russian moon impact rocket was launched on Saturday, September 11, 1959, our accumulated knowledge of the Moon made it seem like a familiar old friend. Observatories around the world had photographed one side of the Moon many times, acquiring the information which, years ago, allowed scientists to name its various terrain features. Thus, when the Russians announced the impact on Monday, September 14th, as being near the Sea of Tranquility, the Sea of Serenity and the Sea of Vapors, scientists of all nations knew the exact location of the impact.

Further proof of the accuracy of our previous findings and historic new information about the Moon were supplied by the Soviet satellite, Lunik III, which passed around the back side of the Moon on October 7, 1959, and from an altitude of about 37,000 miles above the Moon made the first photographs of its hitherto unknown side. The photographs were transmitted by television to earth stations on October 18th, when Lunik III was about 29,900 miles from the Earth.

The Soviets released the moon pictures to the world on October 26th, together with a description of additional Moon terrain features which they have been the first to name. Most prominent among them is the large Sea of Moscow and its Bay of Astronauts. Other features are the Sea of Tsiolkovsky, Lomonosov Crater; Joliot Curie Crater; the Sovietsky Mountain Range and the Sea of Dreams.

The exact path and speed of the lunar impact rocket, as well as the orbital path of the lunar satellite, had to be computed and calculated from knowledge gained prior to the launching of these two historic vehicles. The facts that the rocket made impact within from 120 to 180 miles of its intended striking point and that the satellite completely performed its planned mission indicate the reliability of the knowledge accumulated over the years by astronomers.

However, before we become complacent about how much we know, perhaps we should remember that the Moon is our closest neighbor and that our knowledge of other planets may not be as accurate.

To sense the enormity of space, study carefully the charts of distances, reprinted here through the courtesy of *Air Force Magazine*.

Through the use of telescopes and a vast array of other astronomical equipment, astronomers have accumulated an impressive amount of knowledge concerning our solar system, knowledge which must be be accepted as accurate until such time as man is able to move freely and usefully in space, to corroborate or modify these findings.

By optical observation over long periods of time and by more recent use of such devices as radio and radar telescopes, scientists have been able to chart accurately the size, axial rotation and inclination, orbital path and speed of celestial bodies.

Science long ago discovered that every element possesses an individual light property that falls within a specific portion of the color spectrum. No two elements have the same color response. Thus, when a light reflected from an element is broken down by being passed through a series of prisms, the resulting segment of the color spectrum revealed will identify the element. The instrument used to examine the spectra of bodies, in order to determine their composition, is called a *spectroscope*. The spectra of celestial bodies are obtained by using a *compound spectroscope* which consists of a series of prisms arranged in the arc of a circle and used with a celestial telescope. By following this procedure, scientists have come to know the composition of celestial bodies, even though man has never actually explored them.

Based on present knowledge and considering the elements of the solar system from the Sun outward, these are some of the things we know about space:

The Sun is, in astronomical terms, a main sequence star of spectral type G-zero. It is 93,000,000 miles away from the Earth and approximately 300,000 times as massive as the Earth. It has a surface temperature of about 11,000 degrees Fahrenheit.

The Sun puts out energy constantly in the form of light and heat; in fact, every useful form of energy on the Earth's surface, with the exception of atomic and thermonuclear energy, is either directly or indirectly the result of the storing or conversion of energy received from the Sun.

At various unpredictable times the Sun also produces ultraviolet radiation, radio waves and charged particles, or cosmic rays. Space flight planners are concerned about the possible lethal properties of solar radiation and its effect upon successful space travel during the periods of extreme solar flare activity. It is a subject about which we are constantly learning more from rockets and satellites sending back data.

Some fairly recent information received from measurements made by a series of eight Nike-Asp rockets fired from Point Arguello, California, by Naval Research Laboratory scientists, not only modifies previous knowledge of the Sun, but may well bring further debate on the risks of space travel because of radiation.

The rockets were able to measure radiation with sustained energy levels many times higher than any previously detected. These measurements were made about 140 miles above the Earth, during solar flares.

This new data also suggests temperatures in the solar atmosphere many times higher than that of the Sun's surface — perhaps as much as 100,000,000 degrees Centigrade.

The United States placed a gold-plated satellite in orbit around the Sun in 1959 and, while the satellite will continue in orbit perhaps for centuries, data is not available from it because its solar energy batteries failed after 82 days of operation and consequently the radio reporting device stopped sending information back.

Because of the unpredictability of solar flares occurring, and the length of time required to get rockets launched, the best hope for scientists to obtain the information they want about the initial radiation burst and its rate of decay is to have satellites continually sent into orbit, ready to report instantly.

Each day, each hour, we may add to our knowledge of the Sun and its environment.

Mercury is the planet closest to the Sun and, because this is so, observation of it is extremely difficult. As a result, we have little data on its physical characteristics. For example, we have no precise knowledge of its mass, although our scientists estimate it is one-twentieth the size of the Earth. We do know it is a rocky sphere, about half again as large as the Moon. Mercury always keeps the same side turned toward the Sun, causing that side to be very hot, probably with surface temperatures as high as 750 degrees Fahrenheit. The side which is constantly in darkness is cold enough to retain frozen gases, probably with temperatures as low as absolute zero. Mercury is not known to have any atmosphere and its surface is thought to be similar to that of the Moon.

Venus has baffled scientists for ages, defying the efforts of our best telescopes to get a good look at it. This is because the atmosphere of Venus has white particles held in suspension, making it opaque to all wave lengths of light. The atmosphere is also decidedly turbulent, so its density, due to the suspended particles, is kept in such constant turmoil that no astronomer has ever been able to get a clear view of Venus' solid surface. In dimensions and mass, Venus is slightly smaller than the Earth. Neither free oxygen nor water vapor have ever been detected on Venus but its atmosphere does contain an abundance of carbon dioxide. This is determined by spectrographic analysis of light reflected from the upper part of its cloud deck. Using all known data, scientists presume Venus is a rather bleak place. S. H. Dole, in a paper written in 1956, stated that, on the basis of all available evidence, it may be presumed that the surface of Venus is probably hot, dry, dusty, windy and dark beneath a continuous dust storm; that the atmospheric pressure is probably several times the normal barometric pressure at the surface of the Earth; and that carbon dioxide is probably the major atmospheric gas, with nitrogen and argon also present as minor constituents.

Mars is the planet about which we know the most, and, because of what we know, it is the planet about which we have the greatest curiosity.

Scientists say that human life could not exist on Mars without certain modifications being made in environmental conditions, but they do not ignore the possibility that this may have been accomplished by at least a self-sustaining colony.

We know that Mars, which has a diameter about halfway between those of the Earth and the Moon, undergoes seasonal changes, with a small amount of light ice or frost at the polar caps in winter which melts in summer. Also, through the findings of Professor G. A. Tikhov of the Soviet Institute of Astrobiology, it is evident Mars has vegetable life.

Mars has a rate of revolution upon its axis similar to that of Earth and the inclination of its equator to the orbital path is also very much like that of Earth. Its atmospheric pressure is thought to be about 12 per cent of the Earth's normal amount at sea level. Nitrogen is the major component of the atmosphere.

Considering the estimated climate of Mars, in order for human life to exist there, the Martians would have to be people who could live in a desert area about 12 miles above sea level (compared to Earth conditions), where daytime temperatures would go to 90 degrees Fahrenheit and drop during the night to as low as minus 100 degrees Fahrenheit.

No free oxygen has been detected and there seems to be little or no water on Mars. In spite of this, spectroscopic evidence indicates there is vegetable life on this planet.

Orbiting, instrument-carrying satellites will no doubt add substantially to our present knowledge of Mars.

Jupiter, Saturn, Uranus and *Neptune* are all so similar that one description will suffice for all. Scientists call these the giant planets, for they are all massive bodies with low density and large diameter and they all rotate very rapidly. Spectral information indicates that each of these planets has a rocky core surrounded by a thick shell of ice and covered by thousands of miles of compressed helium and hydrogen. Other elements which have been detected in small quantities are methane and ammonia. Temperatures at the visible upper atmospheric surfaces range from 200 to 300 degrees below zero Fahrenheit.

Jupiter, Saturn and Neptune have a number of satellites which are larger than our Moon and may be as large as Mercury in some cases. Scientists feel these satellites of the giant planets may offer more possibilities for bases for space flight missions than do the parent giant planets.

The Moon, as has been stated, is our nearest celestial neighbor and as such is the prime target for our probing scientific rockets and eventually manned flight to fulfill that age-old dream of soaring to the Moon. Present knowledge indicates that the Moon is dry and dust-covered, with a rocky surface which has mountains higher than those on Earth and many craters, the origin of which is still in debate. Soviet astronomers have reported observing a volcanic eruption on the Moon which may be the key to the crater origin. The Moon has practically no atmosphere and the high mountains are thought to be due to the fact there is no weathering to erode them. The Soviet rocket which made impact on the Moon on September 14, 1959, has supplied additional data which shows the Moon has no radiation belt and no magnetic field. A blanket or belt of low energy ionized gases covers the Moon, making this area very similar to the ionosphere of the Earth.

Pluto is the most outlying member of the known solar system and we have little information about it. It is presumed to be extremely cold and to have a mass and radius approximately 80 per cent of that of the Earth. Beyond this, we can estimate little about that remote planet.

Our solar system contains other important components which fall into four basic categories and which must be considered in any understanding of the solar system.

In the region lying between the orbital paths of Jupiter and Mars is found a group of substantial bodies which astronomers have named *astroids*. It is generally thought that astroids are the remains of a planet, or planets, and they are known to range from a few miles in diameter to almost 500 miles in mean diameter in the case of Ceres, the largest of the group. Some of these astroids leave their native area from time to time and approach within a few million miles of the Earth.

Comets are thought to have heads of frozen gases and bodies of dust and rarefied gases. These collections of orbital material dash into our solar system from the far reaches of space, beyond the orbit of Pluto, and then return from whence they came. Some of them make a periodic appearance, while others may show only once and then are never observed again.

Meteorites are formed of particles of material from space which the Earth attracts in large quantities. Fortunately, most of the meteorites decompose in the upper atmosphere but some reach the Earth's surface. Scientists have made various estimates of the daily amounts of incoming meteorite material, ranging from 25 tons to 1,000,000 tons per day. Meteorites enter the Earth's atmosphere at speeds of up to 50 miles per second and then run into a natural problem similar to the re-entry problem that once plagued our missile builders. Due to their high speed, the meteorites burn in the atmosphere, causing light streaks we call *meteors*. How much of this meteorite material lies in outer space is a question which will probably only be answered by the experiences of space vehicles. It is a question which gives constant concern to our space flight planners.

Another important component of the solar system is dust composed of small particles called *micro-meteorites*. The layer of cosmic dust seems to extend all the way from the Sun to well beyond the orbit of the Earth. Solar radiation causes the dust particles to spiral toward the Sun but the material appears to be continually re-supplied by the waste from comets and collisions of astroids. Meteoritic dust — or micrometeorites — is also a concern of space flight planners.

Not long ago, we had a term which could be applied to any fantastically large number, we called it an "astronomical figure." As we stick a tentative toe over the threshold of space, we discover our language is not capable of describing the vastness that lies before us, an immensity that may be beyond the comprehension of the human mind. Our own solar system is but a minute part of total space.

Our solar system has as its nearest neighbor the star system Alpha Centauri, a double star whose two main components orbit around each other, plus a third star called Proxima Centauri, so named because it is the closest of the group to our Sun. Pluto, in our solar system, is five and a half *light-hours* from the Sun, a distance so great we know little about Pluto. Proxima Centauri, the closest of the Alpha Centauri system, is four and a half *light-years* away.

Our scientists estimate there are from 1 to 10 *billion* such planetary systems in our galaxy. Among these, there must be some planets with atmospheric, climatic and temperature conditions similar to those of the Earth, and we can only speculate that life similar to our own might well exist on these planets.

From our Sun to the center of our galaxy, the distance is 26,080 light-years. From the center of our galaxy to the galaxy containing the great nebula Andromeda, the distance is 2,262,000 *light-years*. In other words, light traveling at 186,000 miles per second takes 2,262,000 years to travel this distance. How many of these galaxies may exist, in all sincerity, only God knows.

As our minds grasp fleeting glimpses of the magnitude of our universe, we may wonder just how much progress we have really made in our quest for knowledge about it. One certainty evolves from this trend of thought. Every student, each boy and girl, from here to eternity, must absorb the available knowledge to the limit of his or her capacity to learn, if human beings ever hope to gain an understanding of the area surrounding them.

2/WHAT WE KNOW ABOUT THE EARTH

As Copernicus concluded back in the days when Columbus was discovering America, we all know that our Earth makes a complete revolution on its axis every 24 hours, giving us night and day, while, at the same time, it is following its orbital path around the Sun, causing winter when it is farthest from the Sun and summer when it is closest, with the shadings of spring and fall in between the two. The intensity and characteristics of the seasons vary with the distance of the Earth's surface from the equator, which is that portion of the Earth always nearest the Sun.

A little over fifty years ago, the Wright Brothers gave the world powered flight and man the means to leave the Earth and fly in the air above it. Since that time, the men of the Air Force have been flying ever higher and faster, until they have reached the very fringes of space. For almost two decades, the three military services and the National Aeronautics and Space Administration have been firing a variety of rockets and ballistic missiles, all of which have continually added to our knowledge of the Earth and its atmosphere.

Three years and one week before the Soviet lunar rocket made impact on the surface of the Moon, on September 7, 1956, to be exact, a quiet, handsome, blue-eyed Air Force captain named Iven C. Kincheloe, Jr., climbed the Bell X-2 rocket-powered experimental aircraft which he was piloting to an altitude of 126,000 feet, almost 24 miles from the Earth, through 99 per cent of the Earth's effective atmosphere. He soared farther into space than any other human being in history had ever gone. This epic flight began and terminated at Edwards Air Force Base, California. On the weekend of July 26, 1958, Captain Kincheloe met his death in the crash of an F-104, also at Edwards. However, on the date the Soviets succeeded in landing a rocket on the Moon, Iven Kincheloe, posthumously held the record for distance traveled into space by a human being. Experimental flights of this type, the routine missions of jet bombers and fighter-interceptors, and the hundreds of data-seeking rockets have all added greatly to our knowledge of the Earth's atmosphere, which is the first barrier to space flight and the last barrier to a safe return to Earth.

To understand the feat accomplished by Captain Kincheloe, we must examine the portion of the

On September 7, 1956, Captain Iven C. Kincheloe, Jr., flew the Bell X-2 experimental rocket-powered aircraft to an altitude of 126,000 feet, through 99 per cent of the Earth's effective atmosphere and farther into space than any other person in history had ever gone.

atmosphere through which he climbed to the fringe of space, then go on to consider the other layers of the atmosphere. He actually passed through two layers and well into the third. On above, there were two additional layers.

Troposphere — The lowest air region of our atmosphere is called the troposphere. It extends upward for about ten miles, and this region is the maximum operational area of our conventional aircraft. The top limit of the troposphere is called the tropopause. Because of the elliptical shape of the Earth, this ranges from 54,000 feet at the equator, to 36,000 feet at the middle latitudes and 28,000 feet at the poles. Very definitely affecting both an engine and a man is the fact that the troposphere is about 80 per cent nitrogen and only 20 per cent oxygen.

Stratosphere — The layer located from 10 to 16 miles up is known as the stratosphere. Temperatures here are about 70 degrees below zero Fahrenheit and artificial environmental equipment is needed for survival. Without a sealed cabin and a pressure suit, Captain Kincheloe's blood would have boiled at about 63,000 feet, due to expanding gases. If a reciprocating aircraft engine carried an oxygen supply to permit operation at this altitude, it would still produce zero power, due to the low barometric pressure.

Mesosphere — Above the stratosphere, on up to about 264,000 feet, or fifty miles, is the mesosphere. Slightly above 100,000 feet, turbojet engines reach their limit of operation; at about 150,000 feet ramjet engines cease to function. Rocket engines can perform freely on into space, the only limit being excessive temperatures. The mesosphere contains a large concentration of ozone which absorbs much of the Sun's ultraviolet radiation, acting as a shield for the Earth from cosmic rays. This absorption process increases the temperatures, and above 150,000 feet it is about 50 degrees above zero Fahrenheit. Above the 50 mile altitude, just outside the mesosphere, the temperature drops to 104 degrees below zero.

Thermosphere — From 260,000 feet, on to 200 or 300 miles above the Earth, the area is called the thermosphere, so named because of the temperatures encountered here. At about 300 miles, the temperature reaches 2,200 degrees above zero! Also, there is extreme electrical activity in this layer. Powerful electromagnetic waves from the Sun constantly bombard atoms and molecules, causing them to become ionized. Because of this action, the thermosphere is also called the *Ionosphere*. Four different layers of ionized particles make up the Thermosphere. Each layer is more ionized than is the next. That is, the

MILES

UPPER ATMOSPHERE AND BEYOND

FEET

Soviet Sputniks I and II
orbit to 560 and 1,056 MILES

American satellite, Explorer
orbits to 1,587 MILES

Research Rockets

2,400 to 4,000 MILES

WAC-Corporal B, Dec. '52
250 MILES

Aerobee-Hi, July '56
163 MILES

Sounding balloon
143,000 FT.

30 —

— 150,000

Manned balloon—
Maj. David Simons,
USAF, Aug. '57
102,000 FT.

Manned aircraft
(air-launched)
Capt. Iven C.
Kincheloe, USAF,
in Bell X-2,
Sept. '56
126,000 FT.

Farside rocket— launched at 100,000 Ft. from balloon

— 100,000

20 —

Manned aircraft
(taking off from
ground)—RAF pilot
in Canberra-B Mk. 2,
Aug. '57
70,308 FT.

Sailplane
44,255 FT.

Aerial combat
in Korean War
35,000-50,000 FT.

10 —

— 50,000

Kite
32,000 FT.

— 40,000

Mount Everest
29,141 FT.

— 30,000

Aerial combat
in World War I
5,000-
15,000 FT.

Aerial combat
in World War II
15,000-35,000 FT.

— 20,000

— 10,000

0

SEA
LEVEL

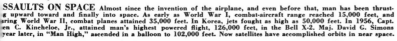

SSAULTS ON SPACE Almost since the invention of the airplane, and even before that, man has been thrust-
g upward toward and finally into space. As early as World War I, combat-aircraft range reached 15,000 feet, and
ring World War II, combat planes attained 35,000 feet. In Korea, jets fought as high as 50,000 feet. In 1956, Capt.
en C. Kincheloe, Jr., attained man's highest powered flight, 126,000 feet, in the Bell X-2. Maj. David G. Simons
year later, in "Man High," ascended in a balloon to 102,000 feet. Now satellites have accomplished orbits in near space.

AIR FORCE Magazine • March 1958

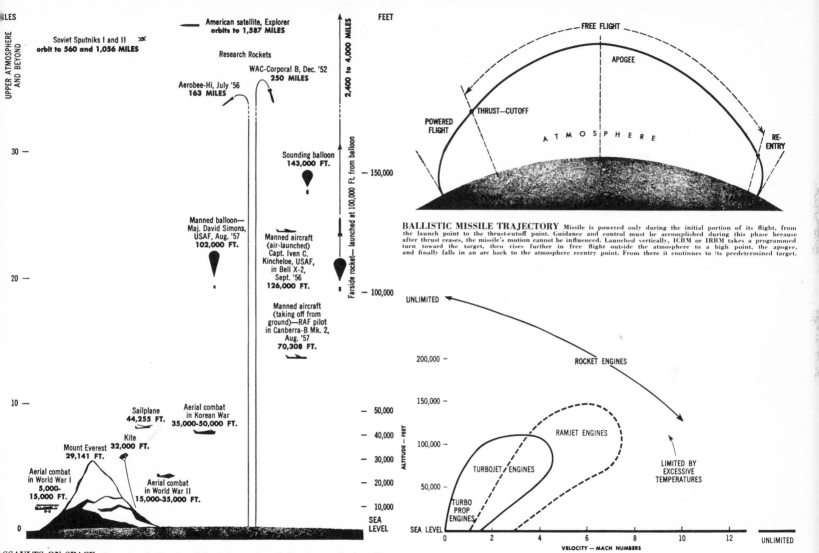

FREE FLIGHT

APOGEE

THRUST—CUTOFF

POWERED
FLIGHT

A T M O S P H E R E

RE-
ENTRY

BALLISTIC MISSILE TRAJECTORY Missile is powered only during the initial portion of its flight, from
the launch point to the thrust-cutoff point. Guidance and control must be accomplished during this phase because
after thrust ceases, the missile's motion cannot be influenced. Launched vertically, ICBM or IRBM takes a programmed
turn toward the target, then rises further in free flight outside the atmosphere to a high point, the apogee,
and finally falls in an arc back to the atmosphere reentry point. From there it continues to its predetermined target.

UNLIMITED

ROCKET ENGINES

200,000 —

150,000 —

RAMJET ENGINES

ALTITUDE — FEET

100,000 —

TURBOJET ENGINES

LIMITED BY
EXCESSIVE
TEMPERATURES

50,000 —

TURBO
PROP
ENGINES

SEA LEVEL

0   2   4   6   8   10   12   UNLIMITED

VELOCITY — MACH NUMBERS

THE LIMITS OF AIR-BREATHING CRAFT Powered flight has taken man and his aircraft to ever-higher
altitudes, and finally to the limits of the most advanced airplanes, powered by ramjets, which run out of air to
"breathe" and push against at about 150,000 feet. At this point rockets take over, carrying their own "air" with them
and offering the mechanical approach to spaceflight because their ability to operate in the vacuum of space is
theoretically unlimited. After today's chemically powered rockets will come nuclear, ion, and even photon propulsion.

ionized particles become more and more concentrated. "D" Region is the lowest layer, then comes "E" (also called "Heaviside"), followed by "F$_1$" and "F$_2$." The electrical activity in the Ionosphere affects radio transmission. It is also considered to be a possible source of propulsion energy which scientists may harness to propel space vehicles. There is no sound in the Thermosphere, or Ionosphere, layer.

Exosphere — The upper layers of the atmosphere, ranging from the Thermosphere to as much as 1,000 miles or more, have been named the Exosphere. There is no definite boundary to the atmosphere; it seems to vary with different conditions. Atmospheric gases have been detected at great distances into space by our probing satellites.

These, then, are things we have learned about the atmosphere which surrounds the Earth. The very complex nature of the atmosphere, with its tremendous changes in temperature and the vast differences in the composition of the individual layers, explains why scientists have found so much difficulty in perfecting a nose cone that could be hurled by a ballistic missile through these atmospheric layers at a speed of many thousands of feet per second, then pass through the same layers again on its return to Earth, still intact and able to perform its mission.

If the problem was great in the development of ballistic missiles, consider the enormity of the problem posed by sending a human being into space and bringing him, or some future "her," safely back to the Earth. There is no question but that such flights will be routine within the foreseeable future, as routine as today's jet flights.

Just as surely as today the professionals of the Strategic Air Command and of our jet airlines casually speed from coast-to-coast and from continent-to-continent in amazing time, so will men soon be traveling in space. It will take time and effort and most of all, *knowledge*. As we learn, we progress.

Men's minds are already in space, they will follow in person.

Radiation belts — Just as the Sun continues to send unexpected bursts of radiation into the solar system and the atmosphere of the Earth, so does the controversy flare and subside over what effect this radiation will have on space travelers. Opinions range all the way from the belief that their vehicles can easily be constructed so that they are safely shielded from radiation effects to the firm conviction that there is virtually no hope for successful space travel.

Due to these probing extensions of man's curious mind, our satellites, his knowledge on this subject is growing steadily. Four of our United States satellites contribute to a better understanding of this phenomenon — Pioneer III, Explorer IV, Pioneer IV and Explorer VII. From the data they have sent back to us, we now know more about the characteristics of this hazard of space.

There are two belts of radiation around the Earth, an inner and an outer layer. The inner belt starts at about 1,300 miles and goes outward into space to about 3,000 miles. This belt is approximately 4,000 miles wide from north to south. The outer belt starts at around 8,000 miles and continues on to over 52,000 miles. This second belt is thought to be approximately 20,000 miles wide from north to south.

A carefully shielded radiation counter carried by Pioneer IV showed the inner belt to contain highly penetrating radiation. Very little radiation was absorbed by the lead shielding which measured up to 0.16 of an inch thick. On the other hand, this shielding was sufficient to absorb practically all of the radiation encountered in the outer belt.

Dr. James Van Allen, for whom these radiation belts are named because of his pioneering in this field, suggests that the data may support a hypothesis that the inner belt contains primarily decay products of neutrons coming outward from the Earth's atmosphere and that the radiation in the outer zone is caused by solar flares and is of much lower energy.

Of concern to scientists is the fact that the radiation problem may not be confined entirely to these two known areas. Extensive radiation has also been detected just a little over 400 miles above the Earth. Only time, and more knowledge, will solve this problem. We are well on the road already, but the way is not easy. We must continue to acquire knowledge so that we may eventually reach the solution.

3 / THE MILITARY IN SPACE

Man may be on the threshold of that period in his development when he arrives at a new concept of warfare which precludes the physical destruction of his enemy and his homeland. Instead, he feels he must produce more economical and effective ways of inflicting the principles and the will of one nation upon another.

This is not because of any inability to make weapons of sufficient power to cause total destruction, rather it is because weapons already produced have the awesome capability of such complete and horrifying devastation that even the most aggressive nation might hesitate to use them. This hesitation could be due to the purely selfish reason that the use of such weapons would create such utter destruction that the conquered area might be denied for years, and perhaps forever, to the conqueror. In the long years scientists now estimate it would take for nuclear radiation to diminish sufficiently to allow occupation of a bombed area by human beings, the ensuing neglect, added to the initial damage to all growth and natural resources, could make land forever valueless.

On June 25, 1959, Dr. John N. Wolfe, Chief of the Environmental Sciences Branch of the Atomic Energy Commission's Biology and Medicine Division, testified before a Congressional subcommittee on the long time ecological effects of nuclear warfare.

Dr. Wolfe stated that, after the hydrogen bombs had done their initial destruction of life and property, Nature would then exact a terrible vengeance on nations which had engaged in this type of warfare. He felt that famine, pestilence and death would begin where the hydrogen bombs left off and continue for perhaps a thousand years to further ravage the violated earth.

Among Dr. Wolfe's predictions on the aftermath of hydrogen warfare were these:

Fires consuming thousands of square miles of forest and grassland, with normal winter snows being the only hope of eventually extinguishing the holocaust.

Mountain glaciers and snowfields melting to provide the water that would flow unhampered down denuded slopes to permanently flood valleys that were once life-sustaining. Entire watersheds forever destroyed.

The creation of new dust bowls and the extension of present ones, with sod destroyed by fire and the earth unprotected from wind erosion.

Plant, animal and human diseases intensified in the unproductive, ravaged areas. Rats and insects multiplying in many isolated places and the human population so weakened by disease and starvation that it could no longer cope with any natural disasters such as floods, blizzards, tornadoes, or even sudden changes of temperature.

Those were the horrible predictions of Dr. John N. Wolfe. The office of Civil Defense reported to the same subcommittee on the probable initial effects of a hydrogen attack.

Almost 50,000,000 Americans, men, women and children, would be dead. Another 20,000,000 would be injured, but with some chance of recovery. About 129,000,000 would be uninjured but subject to the possible effects of radiation.

These appalling estimates of the consequences of modern warfare may be harbingers of the era when man's enlightened mental processes may turn to new and less destructive but more effective ways of waging war.

However, until we have attained that stature, we have no alternative but to keep pace with the progress of our potential enemies and at least maintain a parity in the weapon systems that can deal this fearful destruction. For this reason, our initial efforts towards conquering space must be almost entirely devoted to the urgent goal of developing a military capability out there. To establish a definitive goal in this area poses a baffling and confusing problem. The military is taking an intelligent approach to its solution.

Security will not permit revealing how many companies are presently under contract with the military to study the various perplexing phases of this problem of decision. However, it is permissible to mention the broad study program initiated by the United States Air Force to determine the feasibility of strategic interplanetary systems. Generally, the companies involved devise certain problems which may be encountered and then develop various methods of solving these problems. There is evidence of quite considerable disagreement on many facets of the question among the industry scientists engaged in the program, the potential worth of the Moon in military operations being one of the chief bones of contention.

Some of our scientists feel there has been too much emphasis placed on the military importance of Moon bases; in fact, that the role of the military in space is being greatly overplayed. This group does not say there is no military potential in space, rather that, at the present time, our knowledge is not sufficient to support many of the ambitious plans being advanced. In other words, we are trying to put the cart before the horse and trying to run before we learn to walk.

Others doubt that space vehicles can ever be used as weapon platforms in the same manner in which we have used our conventional aircraft, for the simple reason that so many factors would be working against the possibility of such vehicles having any great degree of accuracy in making impact with a definite target. They point out that contemporary warheads have such terrifying power, even a near miss would have awful results.

Those in favor of strategic military space systems recognize all the problems we face in developing Moon bases and space vehicles, but they still feel the possibilities should be investigated, not on the basis of what we know, but rather because of the many factors we do not know. Many of the unknowns may prove to have great military significance. In other words, they advance the proven theory that with knowledge will come solution. If we do not know how to use space for military purposes, we should carefully visualize every conceivable problem, then find a solution.

It is believed that the study program includes such factors as the use of satellites, space vehicles, missiles of all types, chemical and biological warfare, nuclear power for propulsion, as well as the employment of microwave radiation to develop rays which might cause disintegration of a space vehicle and the possibility of both space platforms and Moon sites as bases of operation for interplanetary travel and strategic activities.

While this study program is going on, our military leaders are following an intelligent plan of development which will give us a military space capability and will allow us to move readily from there toward any future interplanetary strategic system decided upon as a result of the studies being made.

Reconnaissance Spaceship — This reconnaissance vehicle, designed by Krafft A. Ehricke of the Convair Division, General Dynamics Corporation, could be launched in an elliptical course that would take it around the Moon and back to Earth orbit, a course similar to that of the Soviet rocket, Lunik III. The forward section consists of the crew's gondola, radar and antennas. Back in the Earth orbit, an automatic supply system could be used, with fuel tanks being sent up to the satellite by supply rockets.

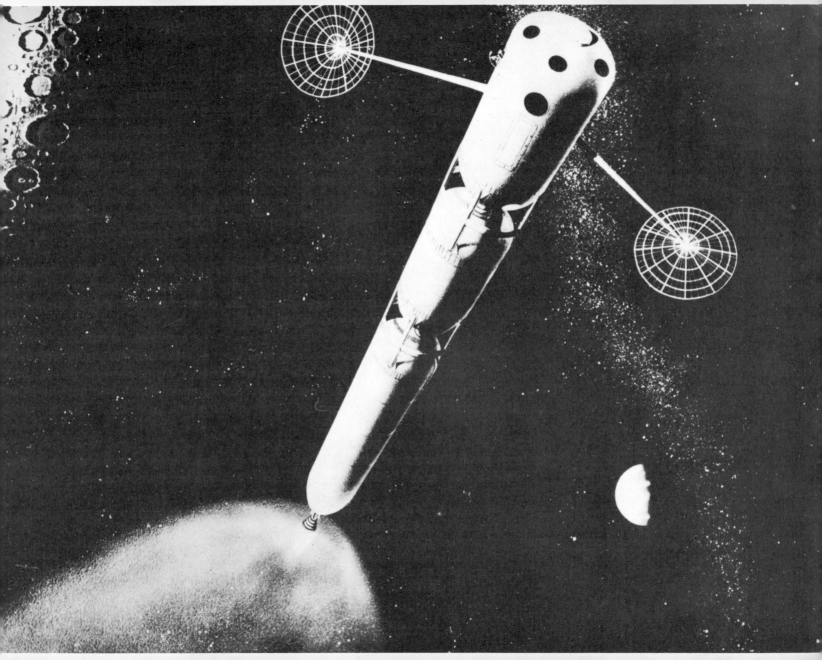

Expanding the established concept of deterrent power as a guarantee of preserving the peace is the present mission of the Strategic Air Command. The plan calls for steadily advancing the capability of offensive weapons. In this category, our immediate attention is given to the development of advanced strategic missile systems, coordinated with manned weapon systems such as the B-52, B-58, B-70 and, in the more distant future, possibly a nuclear-powered bomber. With knowledge gained from such experimental projects as the X-15 rocket powered aircraft, the next step in this evolution from the Missile Age to the Spage Age will bring the manned orbital bomber, such as the Dyna-Soar Project is now developing. Next will come space platforms and, eventually, a complete manned strategic space system for conducting offensive warfare. This final system can then be expanded into a true interplanetary strategic system.

Companion projects to the development of offensive weapon systems — and actually essential to it — are those which will produce means of defense against enemy offensive systems and will give us effective methods of detecting and identifying hostile objects directed toward us at hypersonic speeds. Actually, there is no way to establish a priority between these two requirements because they are so compatible and interdependent that they must be developed together.

In the defensive weapon category, the top priority need is for an effective anti-missile system — a missile defense system against missiles. Hard on the heels of an anti-missile system, we must develop a defense against it which will be an anti-anti-missile system. Both of these systems require the early warning and tracking devices which are necessary to make the systems work. The natural evolution of defensive weapons must lead to a satellite defense system, a satellite inspection system, and, eventually, to a complete manned defensive space system.

Contributing to the success of all the other systems is that one which will give us the capability of effective reconnaissance. Plans include the production of a reconnaissance satellite weapon system, perhaps evolving from an earlier orbital bomber, and a companion infrared alert system. Subsystems will permit visual reconnaissance of the Earth's surface and will make possible accurate mapping and charting of the Earth — and, in time, many of the other planets.

For each of the basic systems — offensive, defensive and reconnaissance — there must be developed means of supporting them. It is from the developments in this category that many of our initial benefits to mankind will come. Quite a few of the methods required for the support of the military mission will have immediate peaceful uses. In the support system, there must be communications satellites, environmental observing and forecasting satellites, an effective means of space navigation, integrated ground acquisition and tracking systems and a method of supplying all systems.

This supply system, which the military calls logistics, must maintain and supply all other systems. Such a system must be able to supply fuel to satellites, space stations and other space vehicles. It must also move them to launching points on the ground and provide prime movers into space in the form of a first stage booster which can be recovered and used again. The system must also develop a means of space transportation of personnel and supplies to acomplish the logistical mission.

All of these long range military plans are based upon our ability to get men into space and to give them the necessary environment to permit them to perform useful functions. The immediate objective of the military, then, is twofold.

First, we must continue to develop to operational level, maintain and steadily improve ballistic missiles, combining them with manned strategic aircraft to form an integrated manned-unmanned offensive and defensive system strong enough to preserve the peace.

Secondly, we must carry on every effort toward getting men and manned vehicles into space and producing the many facets of support methods and equipment required.

An essential contribution to the second phase of the military objective is the continual probing into space for the knowledge we must have to carry on. This includes the study programs, experimental manned craft, our research and development program and the hundreds of rockets and satellites designed to go into space and send back the data our scientists require. This search for knowledge in support of the military objective which will provide immediate benefits to mankind from the fantastic amounts of money, time and energy that necessarily go into the space program.

The urgency of our military requirements will force us to accept new ways of living a better life on Planet Earth.

4 / MAN INTO SPACE

It is anybody's guess when man first conceived the idea of projecting himself into space. For centuries there have been writings, both fictional and serious, of men making trips to the Moon. Who knows what man first felt the urge to fly away from the Earth and get a firsthand look at the mysterious and fascinating bodies of the heavens?

In the never-ending search for knowledge, man is now on the threshold of the intellectual stature which will permit him to fulfill this age-old dream. Among the skeptics, the doubters and the timid there is still not one who will deny the possibility of placing a man in space — and allowing him to perform a useful function while there.

The approach to space has taken two different, yet similar avenues. One is a slow, cautious, step-by-step approach in a vehicle under control of its pilot. The other approach places the space traveler in the role of a passenger whose chief mission initially is survival.

The manned vehicle approach is an extension of the experimental project which allowed Captain Iven C. Kincheloe, Jr., to penetrate the fringes of space in the X-2. It is called the X-15 research program and it is a national effort being conducted jointly by the National Aeronautics and Space Administration, the Air Force and the Navy, in conjunction with the manufacturer of the X-15 research vehicle, North American Aviation, Inc.

In the spring of 1952, the NASA directed its laboratories to study the problems likely to be encountered in flight beyond the atmosphere and recommend methods to solve these problems, After considering laboratory techniques, missiles and manned aircraft, the decision was made in favor of the manned research vehicle, now called the X-15.

The primary research interest of the X-15 is to obtain knowledge of actual flight conditions beyond the Earth's atmosphere, aerodynamic heating and heat transfer and the measurement of heat on structural components.

Engineers believed they had gone about as far as they could with Earth-bound flight simulator studies of the aerodynamic and ballistic controls provided in the X-15. What was needed next was knowl-

Space Age Engineers, the airmen of the future — Joseph Walker, NASA; Major Robert White, USAF; and Scott Crossfield, North American Aviation, Inc. These men fly the X-15 rocket-powered experimental aircraft on flights into space and back.

edge of control requirement at low dynamic pressures found at extremely high altitudes and the determination of applications of the two control systems during a typical mission.

Third, and probably most important, was the wealth of data to be obtained from repeated missions involving exit from and entry into the Earth's atmosphere.

Finally, only man can prove how man will react to space flight. The X-15 test program provides the answers to how he will react to weightlessness, acceleration and deceleration.

The men who were to fly the X-15 were given extensive altitude and other tests, and the North American X-15 flight control simulator was used to familiarize them with flight profiles and all possible emergency conditions which might arise.

From this testing and training, plus research into other human factors, it was concluded that man would not prove a limitation to the high speed, high altitude flight of the X-15. In step with this conclusion, human factors engineers provided maximum protection for the pilot while in performance of his research mission.

For example, there is a built-in safety factor in the high altitudes reached by the X-15. In the event of any unforeseen emergency at those altitudes, the entire ship itself would be utilized as an escape capsule to penetrate the atmosphere. Once back within the denser atmosphere, a conventional ejection would be possible, even at altitudes above 60,000 feet. The pilot's pressure suit will provide breathing oxygen, a compatible pressure environment and wind blast protection during the ejection. A new type of ejection seat will prevent tumbling at excessive G forces. Separation from the seat and the opening of the parachute would be automatic.

The men who fly the X-15 are professional engineers and test pilots, each of whom has acquired thousands of flight hours, testing operational and experimental aircraft, coupled with extensive study and experience in all facets of aeronautical engineering.

North American assigned A. Scott Crossfield and Alvin S. White as project pilots. The Air Force originally assigned the late Captain Iven C. Kincheloe, Jr., to fly the X-15, with Captain Robert M. White as his back-up pilot. With Captain Kincheloe's untimely death in the F-104 crash, Captain (now Major) White became the number one Air Force pilot on the project, backed up by Captain Robert A. Rushworth. The NASA selected three pilots, Joseph A. Walker, John B. McKay and Neil A. Armstrong.

Crossfield was the first person to fly the X-15 in both nonpowered and powered flight, during the course of the program in which the manufacturer was required to make the initial test flights and, after a satisfactory evaluation of the craft's performance, to turn it over to the Air Force. The latter would accept the airplane and, after further test flights, would share the craft jointly with NASA in the research flight test program.

Scott Crossfield, the first man to pilot an aircraft at twice the speed of sound, was born in Berkeley, California, on October 2, 1921. He is a graduate engineer from the University of Washington, with Bachelor of Science and Master of Science degrees. He was research engineer and pilot for NASA from 1950 to 1955. Prior to that, he was chief wind tunnel operator at the University of Washington's Aero Laboratory. Crossfield, the father of five children, made his first flight at the age of twelve and during World War II was a fighter pilot and instructor for the U.S. Navy.

Alvin S. (Al) White, like Crossfield, was born in Berkeley, California, his birth date being December 9, 1918. White is a graduate engineer from the University of California. He was an Air Force fighter pilot and test pilot for eleven years. White flew P-51's in Europe during World War II. He rejoined the Air Force in 1948 and served as an engineer at Wright-Patterson Air Force Base and the Flight Test Center at Edwards Air Force Base. He became a North American test pilot in 1954. He has two children and lives in Palos Verdes Estates, California.

Major Robert A. White was born in New York City on July 6, 1924. He was an Air Force fighter pilot in World War II and the Korean conflict. He has served as a test pilot at the USAF Flight Test Center, Edwards Air Force Base, since 1954. Major White is a graduate of New York University, with a degree in electrical engineering. With his wife and two children, he resides at Edwards Air Force Base.

Captain Robert A. Rushworth was born on October 9, 1924, in Madison, Maine. Captain Rushworth graduated from the University of Maine with a degree in mechanical engineering. During World War II, he was a combat transport pilot, dropping supplies behind the enemy lines. In the Korean conflict, he was a fighter pilot. After that ended, he graduated from the USAF Institute of Technology, at Wright-Patterson Air Force Base, Ohio. Captain Rushworth and his wife have one child. They, too, reside at Edwards Air Force Base.

Joseph A. Walker is one of NASA's most experienced aeronautical research engineer-pilots. He has flown for the government research organization since March, 1945. A graduate of Washington and Jefferson College, with a degree in physics, during World War II, Walker flew combat missions in the Mediterranean Theater. With his wife and three children, he resides at Lancaster, California. He was born in Washington, Pennsylvania, on February 20, 1921.

John B. McKay was born on December 8, 1922, at Portsmouth, Virginia. He graduated from Virginia Polytechnic Institute, with a degree in aeronautical engineering. McKay first joined NASA as a research engineer and in 1951 was assigned as a research engineer-pilot at NASA's High Speed Flight Station, at Edwards Air Force Base. He was a carrier pilot in the Pacific with the Navy in World War II. With his wife and six children, McKay resides in Lancaster, California.

Neil A. Armstrong is the youngest of the assigned X-15 pilots. He was born in Wapakoneta, Ohio, on August 5,1930. He flew 68 combat missions as a Naval jet aviator in Korea. He graduated from Purdue University with a degree in aeronautical engineering and in July1955, was assigned to the NASA High Speed Flight Station at Edwards, as a research engineer-pilot. With his wife and son, Armstrong resides in Juniper Hills, California.

Forrest S. Petersen is a Lieutenant Commander in the United States Navy. He is assigned to the X-15 program as Navy project pilot. Thirty-seven-year-old Petersen is a veteran fighter-test pilot and a graduate of the United States Naval Academy, class of 1945. He served with the fleet until 1946, then applied for flight training and received his gold wings in 1947. He attended the Navy's Post Graduate School, majoring in aeronautical engineering, then entered Princeton University and received his master's degree there. He resides in Lancaster, California, with his wife and two children.

These are the pilots of the X-15. Any young boy who aspires to being the pilot of modern aircraft or spacecraft would do well to note the educational background of these men. They are engineers and scientists, with a good basic knowledge of their work, as well as experienced airmen. These are the men who are pushing back the frontiers of space, using knowledge to overcome the barriers.

In May 1959, two monkeys named Able and Baker were shot into space and returned safely to Earth. To record their reactions to space flight, each monkey was encumbered with numerous instruments. These were promptly put to use in the medical field and promise to revolutionize the diagnostic procedures. Tiny transducers that can instantaneously report the slightest change in heart action, body temperature

Powered for Space — Cut-away diagram shows the compact arrangement of the various parts of the X-15 rocket-powered experimental aircraft.

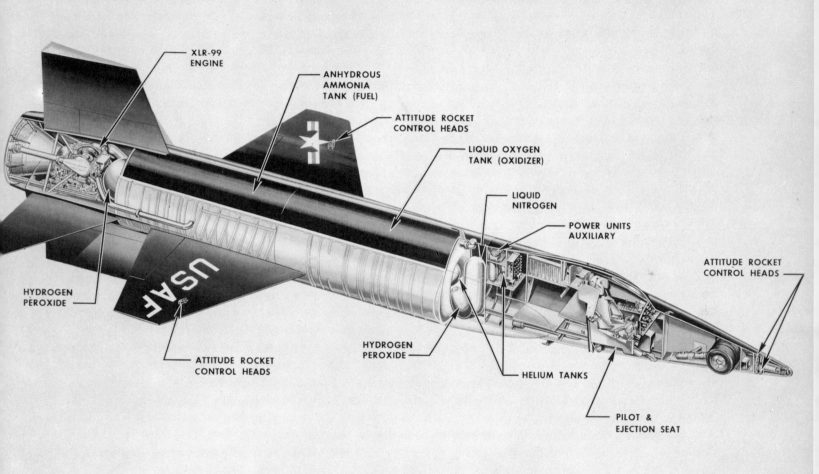

XLR-99
ENGINE

ANHYDROUS
AMMONIA
TANK (FUEL)

ATTITUDE ROCKET
CONTROL HEADS

LIQUID OXYGEN
TANK (OXIDIZER)

LIQUID
NITROGEN

POWER UNITS
AUXILIARY

ATTITUDE ROCKET
CONTROL HEADS

HYDROGEN
PEROXIDE

USAF

ATTITUDE ROCKET
CONTROL HEADS

HYDROGEN
PEROXIDE

HELIUM TANKS

PILOT &
EJECTION SEAT

or nervous system are among the many new devices science has produced to study the human body. Already these are stepping up the pace of medicine. The same instruments were employed in testing the X-15 pilots in a program called human factors study. In fact, the human factors phase of testing and preparation for the X-15 program represents one of the most extensive research projects in aviation history.

Countless tests and experiments were made in flight simulation laboratories throughout the country on every detail of the X-15's mission from the point of view of the human being who would fly it. These included tests of the pilot's equipment, cockpit design, seat, controls, the specially constructed pressure suit and the physical forces that would be exerted on the pilot.

Teams of research engineers and technicians from a special branch of the NASA, Air Force, Navy and North American combined to perform the human factors testing program.

In the USAF Aeromedical Laboratory at Wright-Patterson Air Force Base, pilots and equipment were subjected to scores of centrifuge, pressure and thermal tests. The centrifuge at the Naval Air Development Center, Johnsville, Pennsylvania, was used to simulate maximum G forces expected in the X-15.

Parachutes were tested at the Navy facilities at El Centro, California, and sled runs were utilized for determining seat stability and ejection and wind blast capabilities, at the USAF Flight Test Center at Edwards. NASA and Air Force pilots at the same Air Force Base tried the various types of controls for the ballistic control rockets. These rockets are used to control the flight of the X-15 when it has flown so far through the atmosphere that the air is too thin for the use of ordinary aerodynamic controls.

It is clear that every conceivable precaution was taken to make sure the pilots could fly the X-15 and survive. And from the exhaustive program came the reassuring conclusion that man is not a limitation to space flight.

While the testing of the human beings who fly the X-15 has already given the field of medicine new tools with which to do a faster and more effective job, the actual construction of the craft itself has provided new tools and techniques for industry.

Because of the extreme temperatures to be encountered, both high and low, and occurring almost simultaneously, a very special kind of metal had to be used for the basic construction of the research

Aerial Hitchhiker — Tucked under the right wing of an Air Force B-52, the X-15 is carried to an altitude of 38,000 feet, where it is launched. A special pylon was added to the B-52 wing to support the X-15.

aircraft. Such a material, known to be able to withstand temperatures ranging from 1200 degrees Fahrenheit to minus 300 degrees Fahrenheit, was Inconel X, produced by the International Nickel Company. Although Inconel X was considered a weldable material, no detailed experience in welding aircraft structures with it was available as a test.

Company experts not only developed unique and specific techniques of making structural and leak-proof welds, but they also designed and produced a vast array of specialized welding and handling equipment.

Special techniques of contouring skins were developed, involving the use of hot machining, cold machining, ovens, freezers, cutters, slicers and rollers, all of them applied to brand new methods or renovations of proven techniques.

While the X-15 wears a complete external armor of Inconel X, other metals are used, too. A primary structure of titanium and stainless steel meets any heat that soaks through the nickel alloy outer covering. Aluminum, the old standby of the aviation industry, is used internally, where high heat and high loads are not a problem. About 65 per cent of the X-15 is welded structure and 35 per cent is fastened. Compare this with the 100 per cent fastened structure in current operational aircraft.

Eight major subsystems and components make up the "heart and muscles" of the X-15. They are the engine, propellent system, hydraulic system, primary flight controls, auxiliary power units, ballistic control rockets (for control outside the atmosphere), landing gear and the air conditioning and pressurization system.

The basic engine of the X-15 is the XLR-99, capable of more than 50,000 pounds of thrust. It was developed by Reaction Motors, a division of Thiokol Chemical Corporation of New Jersey. In the initial flight test of the X-15, two RMI-XLR-11 engines, each the same as the single engine used in the X-1 aircraft, were used to give the advantage of tried and proven engines in this phase of the program.

The propellants for the XLR-99 engine are liquid oxygen (LOX) and liquid ammonia. They are fed to the engine by a pressure system causing flow in excess of 10,000 pounds per minute. For comparison, the rate of fuel flow for a modern jet fighter with afterburner, such as the F-100, is from 30,000 to 40,000 pounds per hour — thus the X-15 consumes fuel approximately 20 times faster. Decomposed hydrogen peroxide provides a high-temperature gas which is used to drive a turbine-propelled pump,

On Its Own — Dropped from the wing of the B-52, the X-15 uses its own rocket power to accelerate to speeds in excess of 3600 miles per hour.

to boost the LOX and ammonia to engine manifold pressure. Helium gas is employed for tank pressurization and liquid expulsion.

The primary flight controls of the X-15 are a further development and extention of the conventional controls. They are improved to take increased surface loads, high G forces and high operating temperatures.

On reaching extreme altitudes, where there is not enough air in the thin atmosphere for normal controls to work, control of the X-15 depends upon hydrogen peroxide thrust units which are referred to as ballistic control rockets. These units are located in the nose and wingtips and control the airplane by causing it to move opposite to the direction of the jet streams of gas released at the will of the pilot. Pitch and yaw is controlled by the nose jets, roll by the ones in the wingtips. Together, they enable the pilot to maintain proper flight attitude during the ship's trajectory through thin air.

Landing gear on the X-15 departs from the conventional by using two steel skids on the aft section below the horizontal stabilizers. Dual nose wheels are used to give directional stability during high speed landing. Both the nose wheels and skids are manually retractable into the fuselage for flight and are extended by a mechanical means which uses gravity and the air stream.

The pilot and the delicate instruments in the X-15 are protected from extreme temperatures by a liquid nitrogen air conditioning and pressurization system. The cooling system weighs only 150 pounds, yet it has a cooling capacity of 27,000 btu. (British thermal unit). Newly developed insulating materials complete the design which makes possible the protection of the precious cargo from the tremendous heat during high speed re-entry of the atmosphere.

Many of the X-15's revolutionary features are already finding uses in industry.

The X-15 research program was initiated in the spring of 1952. In October of 1958, the first X-15 was completed and on March 10, 1959, nestled under the right wing of an Air Force B-52, the X-15, with Scott Crossfield at the controls, made a successful first captive flight. By this is meant that the X-15 was not released from the B-52. Three additional captive flights were made on April 1, April 10 and May 21.

The X-15 completed its first glide flight from an altitude of 38,000 feet, with a successful landing on the dry lake bed at Edwards Air Force Base, on June 8, 1959.

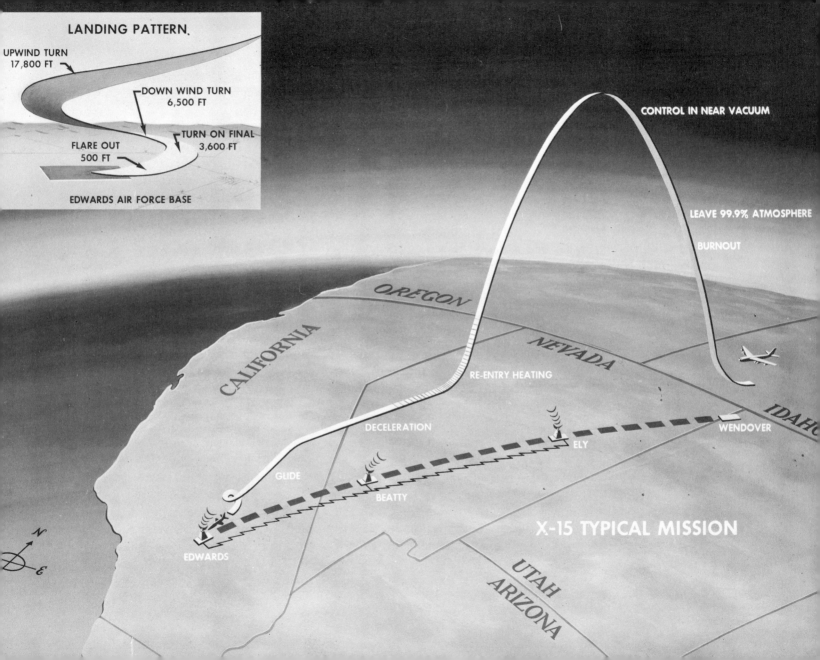

LANDING PATTERN.

UPWIND TURN
17,800 FT

DOWN WIND TURN
6,500 FT

TURN ON FINAL
3,600 FT

FLARE OUT
500 FT

EDWARDS AIR FORCE BASE

CONTROL IN NEAR VACUUM

LEAVE 99.9% ATMOSPHERE

BURNOUT

OREGON

CALIFORNIA

NEVADA

RE-ENTRY HEATING

IDAHO

DECELERATION

WENDOVER

GLIDE

ELY

BEATTY

EDWARDS

X-15 TYPICAL MISSION

UTAH

ARIZONA

N
E

The first of a long series of powered flights was scheduled for July, 1959. These were to prove the airplane's aerodynamic and structural integrity, prior to its being turned over to the Joint Research Committee for maximum performance testing.

On maximum performance missions, the experimental craft is launched about midway between Wendover Air Force Base, Utah, and the Ely, Nevada, radar station. Entering released flight at about 0.8 Mach (500 mph), during the 88-second burnout period of the XLR-99 engine, the X-15 will be accelerated to a speed of about 3600 miles per hour. On maximum altitude flights, the airplane will reach approximately 500,000 feet. Recovery within the atmosphere is made by a 7.33 G pullout from altitudes between 65,000 and 115,000 feet. This will be about five minutes after launch from the B-52. Total free flight of the X-15 is about 25 minutes, with a range of about 400 nautical miles.

An interesting aspect of the X-15 flight test program is the physiological monitoring of the pilots, to determine whole body radiation. These measurements are available for the first time from a human subject flying a research aircraft.

After landing from a high altitude flight, the pilots, on occasion, are rushed to the Los Alamos Scientific Laboratory, about 70 miles north of Albuquerque, New Mexico, where exposure to cosmic ray activity can be measured accurately.

The X-15 is expected to provide important data to aid in the design and construction of operational aircraft capable of shuttling between the earth and satellite or space platforms.

So, with each flight of this small aircraft, 50 feet long, 22 feet in span and 13 feet high, we move nearer to the conquest of space.

The second approach to placing a man in space is a highly scientific program being conducted by the National Aeronautics and Space Administration called Project Mercury. The objective of Project Mercury is to put a manned space capsule in orbit around the Earth, using the Convair Atlas as the vehicle to place the capsule in orbit.

The capsule is designed to be controlled while in orbit and to be brought back safely to Earth, thus supplying essential information on man's capacity to withstand the environment of space.

Every conceivable test known to science has been used in a precautionary program to prepare those

Back on the Ground — The sequence camera shows how the X-15 lands on the Rogers Dry Lake Bed. Steel skids and conventional dual nose wheel are used in the landing.

who man the capsule and the equipment they use for this type of flight into space.

The Atlas Intercontinental Ballistic Missile is a product of the Convair Division of the General Dynamics Corporation and in its role as a strategic weapon it is capable of delivering a nuclear warhead at least 5,500 miles from the point of launching. This gigantic projectile stands 75 feet in the air as it sets on the launching pad, is about 10 feet in diameter, not including the two booster engines, and is capable of roaring toward an enemy target at twenty times the speed of sound.

In its role as a ballistic missile, the Atlas uses two powerful rocket boosters, having a combined thrust of approximately 330,000 pounds. The boosters are used in launching and during the first few minutes of flight. The boosters and their associated equipment are then jettisoned, leaving the sustainer engine with a thrust of 60,000 pounds as the power source for the missile.

After the final engine shutoff, the nose cone separates from the missile and continues on alone to the target, carrying its nuclear load of annihilation.

Because of its proven capability and reliability, the Atlas was chosen as the booster for the Mercury capsule and its precious human cargo.

In place of the nose cone used in strategic launchings, the Mercury capsule is placed atop the Atlas for the beginning of orbital space flight around the Earth. Upon separation from the Atlas booster, the astronaut, as the man in the capsule is called, turns the vehicle into orbital flight position and he is on the way for a controlled orbit around the Earth and an eventual safe return to our planet.

A tremendous amount of research and development activities have gone into the production of the capsule to carry a man into space and accomplish his safe return to Earth.

The Mercury Project is administered by the Space Task Group, with headquarters at the NASA's Langley Research Center in Hampton, Virginia. The project director is Robert R. Gilruth.

Prior to any attempt to put a man in orbit, the program called for many test firings of solid rocket vehicles equipped with various sizes of capsule models, ranging up to the actual capsule size and weight. These tests were to be followed by short range test firings of capsules containing animals and men over ballistic trajectories from Cape Canaveral, using Redstone and Jupiter boosters.

Before tests began at the NASA Pilotless Aircraft Research Station, Wallops Island, Virginia, in the fall of 1958, NASA scientists developed methods for dropping a full scale model capsule from a C-130

Left: The Atlas and manned spaced capsule stand poised for flight, with the Atlas service tower rolled back. It is 85 feet from the base of the booster to the tip of the capsule. (NASA photograph.) **Right:** Artist's conception of Mercury space capsule in orbit over Cuba.

Hercules transport, loaned to the NASA by the USAF Tactical Air Command. Drops were made at Fort Bragg, North Carolina, and over the airfield at West Point, Virginia.

Full scale 2-ton test models are staged out of Langley and loaded aboard the C-130. The test vehicle dropped in a free fall is photographed in descent by two T-33 chase planes, one flying at the same altitude as the C-130 and the other at the altitude where the recovery parachute is deployed.

Two Marine helicopters from Quantico and an NASA crash rescue boat from Wallops Island go to the capsule impact area. One helicopter, directed by the NASA boat and the other helicopter, retrieves the capsule by shackling a line to an eye located on top of the test model.

Detailed studies of the entire operation are made from motion picture film taken by the two T-33's.

The diagram on the next page shows the original design of the capsule and the position of the astronaut. It is probable that the many test firings in the program, plus the information obtained from the X-15 program, will cause some changes to be made in the final version of the capsule.

Naturally, there is a free interchange of data between the X-15 Project and the Mercury Project, as both of them have the same ultimate objective, putting a man usefully in space, although the approaches are different.

When the Mercury capsule is launched, it will have on top of it a plyonlike arrangement tipped with an escape rocket system. If the Atlas booster malfunctions at any time from the pad to staging, an escape rocket can be triggered and it will carry the capsule and its occupant away from the booster. Normal recovery by parachute will then take place.

Reliability tests of the escape system and aerodynamic studies of the capsule-escape combination were conducted from the Wallops Island launching site. With the use of full scale models, scientists determine proper alignment of escape rocket nozzles, as well as dynamic forces on the capsule and escape arrangement during launch and descent.

Behavior of the capsule during flight was studied at Langley and Ames wind tunnels and at the Arnold Engineering Development Center, Tullahoma, Tennessee. Free-flying model studies were conducted at Wallops Island for the same purpose.

At Wallops, small models are subjected to the full velocity range in an investigation of tumbling characteristics, reentry dynamics and afterbody heating. In the wind tunnel program, the NASA em-

This diagram shows the position of the astronaut and the location of the various controls and items of equipment in the Mercury controlled orbit space capsule.

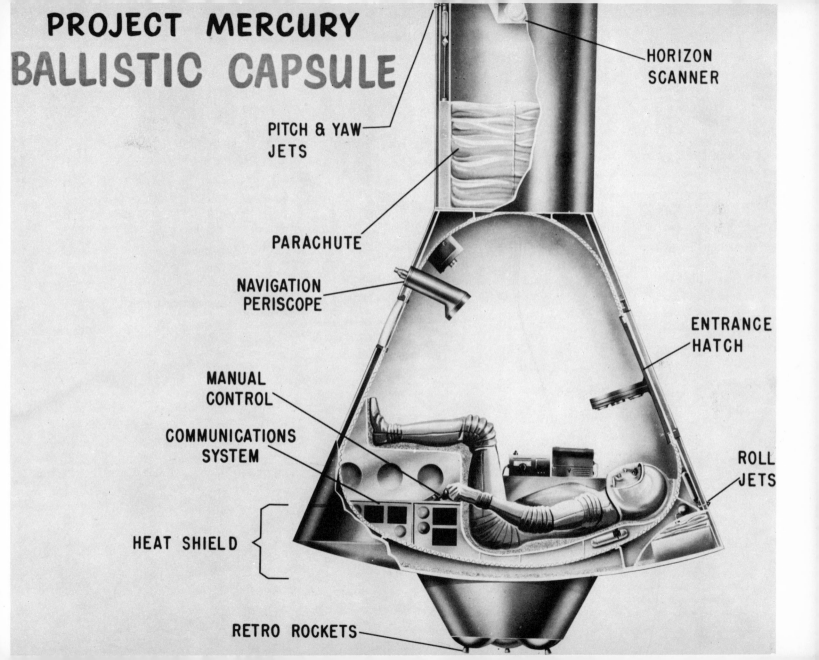

PROJECT MERCURY
BALLISTIC CAPSULE

HORIZON SCANNER

PITCH & YAW JETS

PARACHUTE

NAVIGATION PERISCOPE

ENTRANCE HATCH

MANUAL CONTROL

COMMUNICATIONS SYSTEM

HEAT SHIELD

ROLL JETS

RETRO ROCKETS

ployed the complete range of scaled-down capsule-booster combinations to be used in the build-up program. For example, build-up flights include a capsule-Jupiter combination, while wind tunnel research provided answers to control inputs and trajectories by investigating lift, drag and static stability of the Jupiter-Mercury arrangement in scale models.

At Langley, scientists employ tunnels to determine heat transfer and pressure of heat shield, dynamic stability, afterbody pressures, pressure distribution, lift and drag. The Langley tunnels cover the velocity spectrum from just a few miles per hour to Mach 18, which is 11,000 miles per hour.

At the Ames Research Center, Moffet Field, California, wind tunnels are used to study panel flutter, pressures and heat transfer, static and dynamic stability, lift and drag in the Mach 0.6 (390 mph) to Mach 15.3 (9,950 mph) velocity range.

When the Mercury capsule descends from its orbital flight, it will fall at a velocity of 30 feet per second. Tests in water tanks at Langley show a safe water reentry can be made with the presently-shaped leading face of the capsule. In the event of a ground landing, a crushable material will absorb the impact.

The men who were selected from the many volunteers to occupy the Mercury manned orbital capsule are all pilots superbly adapted to the manned satellite program.

Initially, seven men were accepted for the program, the feeling being that a small number would allow more thorough training and orientation. The seven volunteers provide a variety of technical experience for the project, in addition to training as astronauts.

These are the men selected:

Virgil Ivan Grissom, United States Air Force Captain, was born on April 3, 1926, in Mitchell, Indiana. He is 5 feet, 7 inches tall; weighs 155 pounds. Captain Grissom graduated from Purdue University with a degree in mechanical engineering in 1950. As an F-86 fighter pilot, he flew 100 missions in Korea. He later attended test pilot school and has had several assignments as an Air Force test pilot. He has logged over 3,000 hours, more than 2,000 hours in jets. Captain and Mrs. Grissom have two sons. His hobbies are hunting and fishing.

Malcolm Scott Carpenter, United States Navy Lieutenant, was born on May 1, 1925, in Boulder, Colorado. He is 5 feet, 10½ inches tall; weighs 160 pounds. Lieutenant Carpenter is a graduate of the University of Colorado, with a degree in aeronautical engineering. He has completed several Navy train-

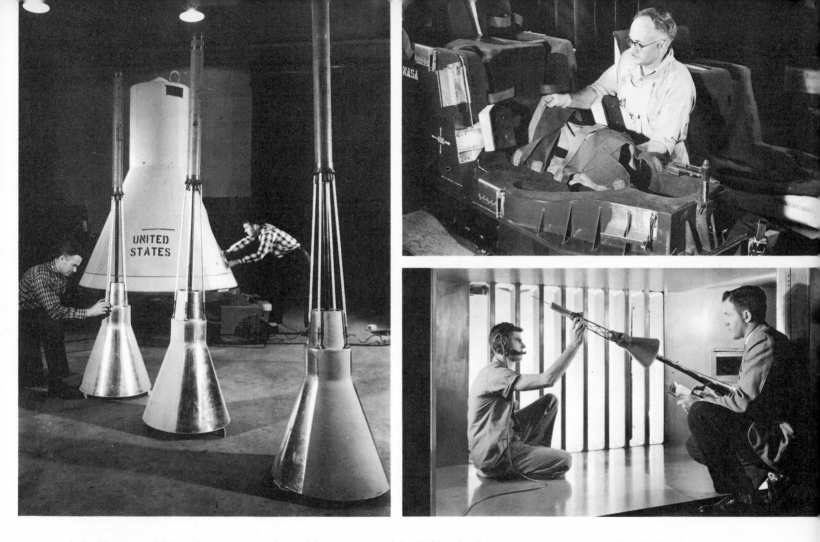

Left: Three one-third scale space capsule models are prepared by NASA scientists for escape system testing. In the background is a full scale model to be used in similar tests. Upper right: NASA scientists develop contoured couches as part of the human support program of Project Mercury. Fitted to the astronaut who will use it, the couch is made of foam plastic and fibrous material. Lower right: Two NASA scientists check one-ninth scale capsule with escape system under pressure tests. The pylonlike escape system is designed to pull the capsule and its occupant away from the booster in case of booster malfunction.

ing programs and has extensive experience as a Navy test pilot. He has almost 3,000 hours flying time, over 300 hours in jets. He was a combat pilot in the Korean conflict. The Carpenters have four children. His hobbies are skin diving, archery and water-skiing.

Donald Kent Slayton, United States Air Force Captain, was born on March 1, 1924, in Sparta, Wisconsin. He is 5 feet, 10½ inches tall; weighs 160 pounds. Captain Slayton graduated from the University of Minnesota in 1949, with a degree in aeronautical engineering. He flew 56 combat missions in B-25's in Europe during World War II. He also flew seven combat missions over Japan. After graduation from college, Captain Slayton was employed as an aeronautical engineer by Boeing Aircraft Company, returning to service with the Air National Guard in 1951. He has extensive experience as an instructor pilot and as an experimental test pilot, assigned to the USAF Flight Test Center at Edwards Air Force Base. He has flown all jet fighter type aircraft built for the Air Force. He has about 3,500 flying hours, more than 2,000 in jets. The Slaytons have one son. The captain's hobbies include hunting, fishing, shooting, archery, photography and skiing.

Leroy Gordon Cooper, Jr., United States Air Force Captain, was born on March 6, 1927, in Shawnee, Oklahoma. He is 5 feet, 9½ inches tall; weighs 150 pounds. Captain Cooper attended the University of Hawaii for three years and received a degree in aeronautical engineering through the Air Force Institute of Technology at Wright-Patterson Air Force Base, Ohio, in 1956. He entered the Marine Corps after graduation from high school, attended the Naval Academy Preparatory School and was a member of the Presidential Honor Guard in Washington, D.C., immediately before his discharge in 1946. While at the University of Hawaii, he received a commission in the United States Army. He transferred his commission to the Air Force and was recalled for flight training in 1949. He flew F-84's and F-86's in Germany and was later assigned to the USAF Experimental Flight Test School, from which he graduated in 1957. He was assigned duty in the Performance Engineering Branch of the Flight Test Center at Edwards Air Force Base, conducting flight tests of experimental aircraft. He has over 2,400 flying hours, about 1,500 in jets. The Coopers have two daughters. The Captain's hobbies are photography, riding, hunting and fishing.

Alan Bartlett Shepard, Jr., is a Lieutenant Commander in the United States Navy. He was born on November 18, 1923, in East Derry, New Hampshire. He is 5 feet, 11 inches tall; weighs 160 pounds.

46

The Astronauts — Displaying a model of the Atlas Booster and the Mercury Capsule are the men selected and trained to take the capsule into orbit. Seated, left to right, Virgil Grissom, Malcolm Carpenter, Walter Slayton and Leroy Cooper, Jr. Standing, left to right, Alan Shepard, Jr., Walter Schirra and John Glenn, Jr.

Commander Shepard attended Admiral Farragut Academy, Toms River, New Jersey, for one year, then entered the United States Naval Academy at Annapolis, graduating in 1944. He graduated from the Naval War College, Newport, Rhode Island, in 1958. He served on the destroyer *Cosgrove* in the Pacific during World War II, then entered flying training, receiving his wings in 1947. He has served various assignments as a fighter and night fighter pilot, has taken part in high altitude tests and those for flight suitability of aircraft for carrier use, and he has participated in Naval trials of the first angled carrier deck. He has over 3,600 hours' flying time, over 1,700 hours in jets. Commander and Mrs. Shepard have two daughters. His hobbies are golf, ice skating and water skiing.

Walter M. Schirra, Jr., is a Lieutenant Commander in the United States Navy. He was born on March 12, 1923, in Hackensack, New Jersey. He is 5 feet, 10 inches tall; weighs 185 pounds. Commander Schirra attended Newark College of Engineering for one year before entering the United States Naval Academy, from which he graduated in 1945. In the Korean conflict, he was an exchange pilot with the 154th USAF Fighter-Bomber Squadron and flew 90 combat missions with that outfit. He has been project officer for several Navy jet aircraft and an instructor pilot. He assisted in the development of the Sidewinder air-to-surface missile. He has over 3,000 hours flying time, more than 1,700 hours in jets. Commander and Mrs. Schirra have a son and daughter.

John Herschel Glenn, Jr., is a Lieutenant Colonel in the United States Marine Corps. He was born on July 18, 1921, in Cambridge, Ohio. He is 5 feet, 9½ inches tall; weighs 180 pounds. Colonel Glenn attended primary and high schools in New Concord and Muskingum College. He graduated from the Naval Aviation Cadet Program and was commissioned in the Marine Corps in 1943. During World War II, he flew 59 combat missions. In Korea, he flew 63 missions with Marine Fighter Squadron 311 and, as an exchange pilot with the Air Force, flew another 27 combat missions. Colonel Glenn downed three MIG's in combat along the Yalu River during the last nine days of fighting in Korea. He has been awarded the Distinguished Flying Cross five times and holds the Air Medal with 18 clusters for his service during World War II and the Korean conflict. He has over 5,000 hours of flying time, more than 1,500 of it in jets. His last assignment was with the Fighter Design Branch of the Navy Bureau of Aeronautics in Washington, D.C. The Glenns have a daughter and a son and the family hobbies are boating and water skiing.

Mercury Astronaut Leroy G. Cooper (left) experiences 13 seconds of weightlessness in an Air Force C-131B airplane. Cooper and Dr. Edwin Vail of the Wright Air Development Center wear full pressure suits as the airplane coasts over a parabolic arc to produce the zero gravity effect.

These are the astronauts, all men with an excellent combination of years of flying experience, educational training and physical characteristics that suits them to become the space pilots of tomorrow.

While engineers, technicians and scientists were busy developing the vehicle which they were selected to pilot, the astronauts were engaged in a program of training, indoctrination and education, to equip them with a wide range of technical knowledge and skills required to pilot the nation's manned orbital capsule.

The initial phase of the astronaut program was broken down into six areas of activity:

1. *Education in the basic sciences* — This is essentially an academic educational program which includes instruction in astronautics, particularly ballistics; trajectories, fuels, guidance, and other aspects of missile operations; basic aviation biology; the space environment, astronomy, meteorology, astrophysics and geography, including the techniques for making scientific observations in these areas.

2. *Familiarization with the conditions of space flight* — This phase of training was designed to familiarize the astronauts with the heat, pressure, G force levels and other special conditions of space flight. It includes periodic simulated flights in centrifuges and pressure chambers, weightless flying, training in human disorientation devices, the development of techniques to minimize the effects of vertigo and experiments with high heat environments.

This part of the training program is providing data on the ability of the astronauts to contribute to system reliability under the conditions to be encountered during flight; the psychological and physiological effects of the normal and various emergency conditions which may be encountered during flight; and the requirement for the support and restraint systems, the environmental control system and the crew space layout.

3. *Training in the operation of the Mercury Space Vehicle* — The objective of this segment of the program is to provide a thorough knowledge of the Mercury vehicle and its functions, including the development of the skills required to control the capsule during flight, technical knowledge of boosters, propulsion systems and ballistics, and familiarization with the test range, tracking and recovery systems. During this period, the astronauts study the onboard capsule equipment and its proper function, including the development of skills in testing and maintaining the scientific equipment, environmental control system and life-support equipment.

50

Below: Atlas Booster Blockhouse Scene — Engineers and technicians seated at a portion of the U-shaped bank of control consoles during an Atlas countdown. Here Atlas subsystems are checked out remotely during the preparation of the booster for firing. Activities on launching pad are observed on television screens, upper right. Right: Atlas Launch Pad —An Atlas ICBM, similar to Mercury Capsule booster except for type of nose cone, stands on the launching pad, ready for firing. Astronauts become familiar with all phases of launching.

4. *Participation in the vehicle development program* — Each of the astronauts has been assigned to a system or subsystem of the Mercury vehicle. In this work, he acquires specialized knowledge of value to the entire group. This material is exchanged in a series of informal seminars.

Actual work on the vehicle development program by the astronauts provides limited augmentation of the Space Task Group staff, in addition to giving the astronauts an intimate knowledge of all aspects of the Mercury vehicle.

5. *Aviation flight training* — The Mercury astronauts continue to maintain their proficiency in high performance aircraft through an aviation flight training program. Continued operation of high performance aircraft gives them additional altitude acclimatization, instrument flight training and the physiology of high altitude, high speed flight.

6. *Integration of astronaut and ground support and launch crew operation* — Familiarization with the operation of ground support equipment and launch crew duties will be accomplished in coordination with the agencies providing boosters and launch facilities. Training in the operation and use of ground support equipment and observation of launch procedures provides the astronaut with complete knowledge of the launch phase of the Mercury flights.

All the existing research, development, training and test facilities of the armed services, industry and educational institutions throughout the country are being utilized for maximum effectiveness at minimum cost. A number of experts in the many scientific and technical subject areas give lectures to the astronauts during this educational program.

The concentrated astronaut education program began with over-all orientation briefings by members of the Space Task Group staff. While assigned to the Langley faculty, the Mercury astronauts work as integrated members of the NASA Space Task Group.

Each of the astronauts is detailed to the NASA by his respective military service. The men are still on active duty and receive military service pay, being on duty with NASA on a full-time basis as they prepare to move on into space.

As short a period ago as a year or two, we tended to look at some of the predictions of our scientists

Left: Nonstop Space Liner — Huge rocket with third stage a detachable glider which would return to Earth after reaching outer space. Rest of rocket contains crew gondola and nuclear engine. Upper right: Gondola, containing crewmen, continues on to Moon, pulled by nuclear engine, as glider returns to Earth. Lower right: Gravitational field of the Moon assists in making lunar landing, with nuclear engine acting as a retrorocket to ease landing impact.

in the same light with which we regarded science fiction. After considering the X-15 program and Project Mercury, some of these predictions now come into better focus and make a more logical impression upon the nontechnical mind.

One scientist who has spent many years thinking in the future, designing and describing things to come, is Krafft A. Ehricke of the Convair Division of the General Dynamics Corporation.

In February of 1958, Convair released to the press some photographs of an artist's conceptions of a nonstop space liner, suggested by Mr. Ehricke when he addressed the third annual Jet Age Conference of the Air Force Association in Washington, D.C. Today, this nonstop space liner seems well within the realm of possibility.

According to Mr. Ehricke, the rocket ship pictured on the next page, represents an application of controlled nuclear energy to space flight which would allow men to make direct flights from the earth's surface to the moon and closer planets.

The bottom stage is a rocket-powered glider, fueled with gasoline and liquid oxygen. The pilot would ride in the attached capsule that could be jettisoned for emergency escape.

Between the glider and the upper stage is a cylindrical adapter structure that holds the two sections together. Inside this adapter are a nuclear power plant and a gondola housing space crewmen. After leaving the Earth's atmosphere, the glider is detached to return to Earth. The adapter structure and the fairing atop the upper rocket would then be jettisoned.

Next, the gondola containing the crew would unreel cable to assume a position 1,000 feet from the nuclear powered upper stage (see picture on next page). This distance is adequate, says Mr. Ehricke, to protect the crewmen from radiation hazards. The crew then would start the nuclear engine, consisting of a nuclear pile and rocket motor fed with liquid hydrogen. Antennas for navigation and communications would be carried as outriggers.

As the glider disappears toward Earth, the gondola, pulled by nuclear power, would continue on to the Moon, landing gently on the three pads showing at the bottom of the gondola. The nuclear engine would then act as a retrorocket to lower the crewmen slowly to the surface.

From the present state of our knowledge regarding satellites and orbital paths, our scientists now say the theory of the space platform is entirely feasible. A structure too large to be placed in orbit as a

Orbital Passenger Craft, featuring a recoverable first stage booster and a third stage which could act as a manned glider, with a pilot and four passengers. Craft could operate between Earth and orbiting satellites.

unit could be erected, piece by piece, in space, with workmen, supplies and equipment being shuttled back and forth between the satellite and Earth.

The refueling of satellites and even the changing of crews of manned satellites are other activities well within the realm of possibility.

Mr. Ehricke, in his various studies leading to new applications of the possibilities of space flight, has designed a whole series of space vehicles to meet the numerous needs of future space activity. One of these vehicles is a shuttle craft which would be used to carry personnel to a satellite station.

The space personnel carrier is a three-stage vehicle, powered by a chemical rocket. It is 130 feet long and would be launched vertically from the Earth. The first two stages would be dropped off after their fuel was expended, at a point where the vehicle would be well beyond the Earth's atmosphere and gravitational field, and the winged third stage, carrying a pilot and four passengers, would continue on into the satellite orbit. The third stage is designed as a glider, so it could be used to carry personnel from the satellite back to Earth.

Ehricke has also designed a similar vehicle which would use nuclear power for propulsion, giving it almost unlimited range and time of operation as far as fuel is concerned.

Mr. Ehricke's series of vehicles would operate at 600-mile altitudes, with the shutle craft servicing orbital observation satellites and space platforms from which unmanned reconnaissance missions could be launched to the Moon and nearby planets.

Plans call for the first stage booster to be recoverable after use. Following burnout, it would be jettisoned from the space vehicle and, at some point back in the Earth's atmosphere, a parachute would open, lowering the stage gently back to Earth where it would be recovered and used again. This method of re-use of the first stage booster is generally recognized as an essential requirement of future space activities because of the economic factor. Cost of missile and vehicle launching would thus be drastically reduced.

The tremendous amounts of electrical energy located in the ionosphere hold the interested attention of our scientists. The potentialities of using this energy for communications systems are under study and consideration by many groups.

Our knowledge of this area, gained from probing rockets and data-seeking satellites, has already

Ion-Propelled Space Vehicle, deriving its power from the elements of the ionosphere, as envisioned by Rocketoyne engineers as a weekend hobby.

found an application in the communications field, a use which is certain to be developed further.

Radio stations are now in operation which use an ionosphere scatter system for transmission and reception. The radio wave is beamed to the ionosphere, from which it bounces back to several points on the Earth's surface, where it is received with extreme clarity. Study of the electromagnetic field also reveals the possibility of utilizing constant magnetic paths for radio transmission and reception at great distances with a clarity never known to present shortwave radio communication. So far, the ionosphere scatter system is being used chiefly for electroteletype transmission in the 20 to 30 megacycles band of the frequency spectrum, but it holds great promise for other types of transmission, perhaps even in the television band. This is another byproduct of space effort already beginning to serve mankind.

The ionosphere also interests scientists as a possible source of energy for the propulsion of space vehicles. While we have a long way to go in our quest for knowledge before such a possibility becomes a reality, engineers have already given much thought to the subject and have advanced ideas along those lines.

For example, a group of preliminary design engineers from Rocketdyne, a division of North American Aviation, started a weekend hobby project to consider the propulsive use of the ionosphere. They came up with an ion-propelled vehicle design which would develop ounces of thrust through discharge of high velocity particles. They believe that, in outer space, ions would propel a three-thousand-pound vehicle at speeds of several thousand miles per hour.

There is no question but that the ionosphere and its tremendous natural energy has great possibilities for utilization. The key of our growing knowledge will soon open this door wide to the eager intellects of our scientists.

As we noted earlier, the Sun is the source, either directly or indirectly, of practically all usable energy on Earth except atomic and thermonuclear energy. Men have always been interested in the obvious logic of using the Sun directly as a source of energy, to run motors and machines of various kinds. Many such devices have been designed and built and several of them are currently in operation.

The one big problem in the earthbound uses of the Sun's strength directly is the cloud cover which plagues the Earth and, sooner or later in any area, will hide the Sun and break direct contact with it.

Once outside the Earth's atmosphere, or far enough into it to leave behind the cloud cover, the Sun

Solar Energy Vehicle — This is a proposed space vehicle which would use solar radiation by collecting the sun's heat to concentrate energy in a working fluid.

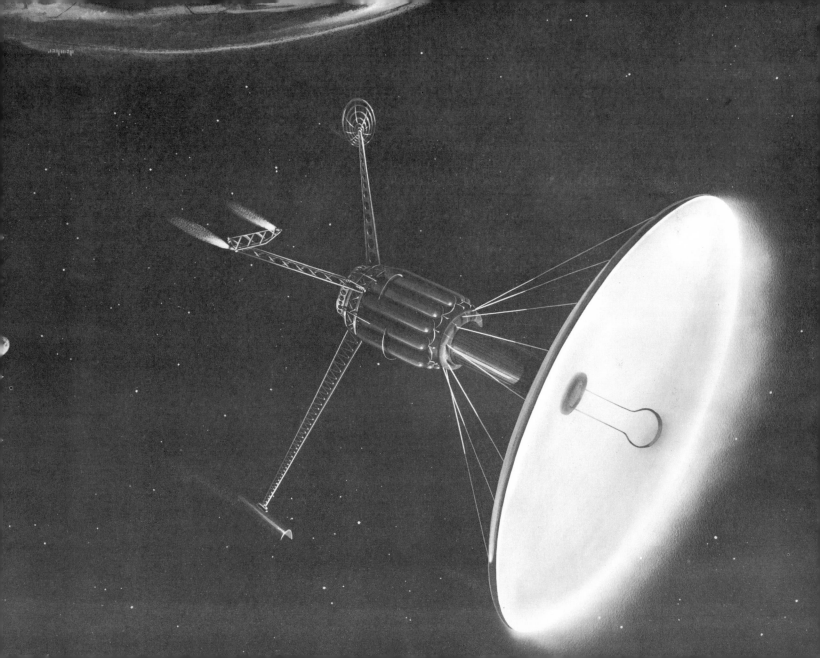

becomes a constant and reliable source of energy for direct use. Solar batteries have been employed in many of our satellites to operate radio transmitters and other devices used in reporting data back to Earth. While there have been some failures in this type of equipment, the Sun is a logical source of energy for devices of this kind.

The Sun is also considered as a source of propulsive power for space vehicles. One popular proposal is a solar radiation system that would collect the Sun's heat with an optical system to concentrate energy into working fluid. This concept uses a big mirror for heating, that is, for collecting maximum heat from the Sun and concentrating it in the area of use. A suggestion by Rocketdyne engineers visualizes a vehicle with rockets in the rear, able to incline freely in any direction 360 degrees, so the mirror would always face the Sun. (See next page.)

The possibilities for the utilization of the energies and the elements of space are endless. Slowly but surely, our scientists, engineers and technicians will develop the methods to do this. As our knowledge grows, so will our ability increase to take advantage of the forces of space. As we learn more and more about these forces, the agile minds of men will find uses for them. And it is reassuring to realize that our space program cannot help but bring us this knowledge which will lead to peaceful and enjoyable uses of space.

5 / PROBING SPACE

Space exploration through the use of satellites, probes and various types of sounding rockets continues at an ever-increasing pace as the demands for new information become more critical. The constant pressure of Soviet scientific progress is forcing the United States to step up the tempo, in order to keep in step with the times.

The scores of research vehicles in use and planned are so numerous that individual consideration is not possible within the limited confines of this book. However, we can discuss the various groups of vehicles, examine the missions they are intended to perform and perhaps look more closely at one or two of the typical devices.

In very general terms, these are some of the knowledge-seeking categories:

Earth Satellites — Several of these have already been placed in orbit with varying results and we certainly can expect many more from time to time as we carry on a stubborn and necessary quest for information about the immediate area around the Earth, an area which represents the first big step into space and the final obstacle to a safe return.

Lunar probes — A few of these probes have already been made but more are sure to come as we need more detailed data on the Moon and its environment.

Deep Space Probes — By "deep space" we mean, initially at least, probes shot at Venus. The first of these is designed to see data on Venus' surface and atmosphere. A preceding high altitude Earth satellite was scheduled to get preliminary information before the actual firing of the Venus probe. The next step in the process is a Venus satellite to report back further data. Later deep space probes will be directed at other planets in our solar system.

Sounding Rockets — As many as from 50 to over 100 of these sounding rockets can be expected yearly. As specific data needs are revealed, the fastest and most economical method of meeting these needs is to fire sounding rockets.

The devices listed so far are under the supervision of the National Aeronautics and Space Administration, and they are being used to study the following aspects of space:

The Earth's Atmosphere is a prime target of these scientific devices. We need to know more about the structure and composition of the atmosphere, especially as to daily, geographic and seasonal changes that may take place. We also want to know about the relationship between surface meteorological conditions and the structure and dynamics of the upper atmosphere.

The Ionosphere — We are particularly interested in getting electron density profiles at altitudes above the F-2 region (about 180 miles into space). We are curious about latitude and time variation of electron density and other phenomena known to exist in this atmospheric layer. Probably, a polar-orbiting satellite beacon can supply this data.

High Energy Particles — In this area of concern, data on the types, distribution and the kinds of action produced in the Earth's atmosphere by the high energy particles is of top priority.

Theory of Relativity — At least one satellite carrying a precisely accurate clock will be launched as an initial test of the theory of relativity as it pertains to the universe.

Electric and Magnetic Fields — Because of the indications that these fields may be both useful and harmful to the space traveler and because there is evidence they may be used to advantage in radio and other types of electronic transmission, we want to know more about them. We are also interested in the ring currents existing above the ionosphere and the relation of these currents to magnetic storms.

Gravitational Fields — A satellite in a very high orbit for a long period of time would be designed to obtain precise geodetic data to let us have a better understanding of the Earth's gravitational fields.

Astronomy Studies — Even with the great progress in telescopes and astronomical equipment, there are still some areas which the world's oldest science has never been able to explore. Scanning satellites and rockets are intended to explore the infrared and high-energy gamma ray spectral regions. Rockets are also intended to examine the nebulosities in the far ultraviolet region, discovered during the International Geophysical Year. The next step in these studies is to be a satellite observatory.

A scanning satellite will also record the high atmosphere emission caused by charged particles interaction and photochemical reactions.

Coordinated with the space exploration programs of the National Aeronautics and Space Administration (NASA) are those of the Advanced Research Projects Agency (ARPA). Major projects of the ARPA are these:

Discoverer — This program is a follow-up to the discontinued Pied Piper reconnaissance satellite project and consists of a series of firing, mostly from the Pacific Missile Range. The purpose is to develop new systems and techniques for producing and operating space vehicles. Later firings in the series were scheduled to carry biomedical experiments in support of Project Mercury.

Communications Satellites — In a program beginning with several experimental versions, this activity was intended to lead to fixed satellites being established 22,000 miles out, to relay radio, television and teletype messages. One of the earlier launchings was called the Score Satellite. It was an Atlas missile, placed in orbit and carrying about 168 pounds of communications equipment. A number of ground-to-satellite and satellite-to-ground communications were made before the Atlas came to the end of its short-life orbit.

Meteorological Satellites — This was an original ARPA project, later transferred to NASA. The purpose of these satellites is to study meteorological conditions in the Earth's atmosphere and to develop a permanent satellite system for observing and reporting weather conditions, leading to more accurate and reliable weather predictions.

Navigational Satellites — The first of these satellites was designed to carry a 150-pound instrumentation package and to stay in orbit about two or three months. The purpose of the program is to develop an all-weather satellite system of determining positions at sea or in the air around the globe.

Midas Satellite — This project is intended to develop a missile defense alarm system. Satellites in orbit around the Earth would detect any ballistic missile launchings through the use of infrared and other techniques.

Those are the general programs of NASA and ARPA for exploration and development. Also, both Project Mercury and the X-15 Program are projects of NASA.

Through the firings already made in carrying out the various phases of the NASA-ARPA programs, the public has become familiar with the names of the satellites in the several series, such as Vanguard, Explorer and Pioneer.

Vanguard I was placed in orbit in March of 1958 and, carrying only a solar battery radio and equipment which gave it the ability to sense gross temperature changes, it still has contributed much important data. It has provided new information on the Earth's shape and orbital information from it was used to locate precisely new land masses.

The launching vehicle was the Martin-Vanguard test vehicle. In February of 1959, a full-size 21-inch sphere was placed in orbit by Vanguard. It contained infrared cloud scanner devices which gave new information on the cloud cover around the Earth.

The Explorer series of satellites began with payloads of about 30 pounds each. These were launched by Jupiter-C missiles and they confirmed the existence of the radiation belts and delivered back new data on them. The instrumentation used was developed by Dr. James Van Allen and his associates at the State University of Iowa.

One of the Explorer satellites of unusual design will be discussed in detail later.

In the Pioneer series, the first vehicle was intended to place an 84-pound instrumentation load in the vicinity of the Moon but it actually reached only about 71,300 miles from the Earth. It was launched by a modified Thor-Able missile. However, radiation data was collected which produced the suspicion that a second radiation band existed, a fact later confirmed.

Pioneer III was launched to an altitude of 63,000 miles on December 6, 1958, and while it also fell short of the intended Moon vicinity, it did supply radiation data from both of the belts, confirming and adding to earlier findings.

Pioneer IV was placed in orbit around the Sun, being launched March 3, 1959. On July 16, another Pioneer vehicle was intended to put a heavy composite radiation satellite around the Earth but it failed on launching and was destroyed five seconds after leaving the pad.

Launching of all Pioneers, after the first one, was by a modified Jupiter missile called Juno II.

This composite instrumentation package which failed to get into orbit in July, 1959, was later placed in orbit in October, 1959, from the Air Force Missile Test Center at Cape Canaveral, and was named the Explorer VII.

In order to better understand these numerous satellite vehicles, and some of the scientific functions they are supposed to perform, we will now consider two specific satellites.

THOR-ABLE III

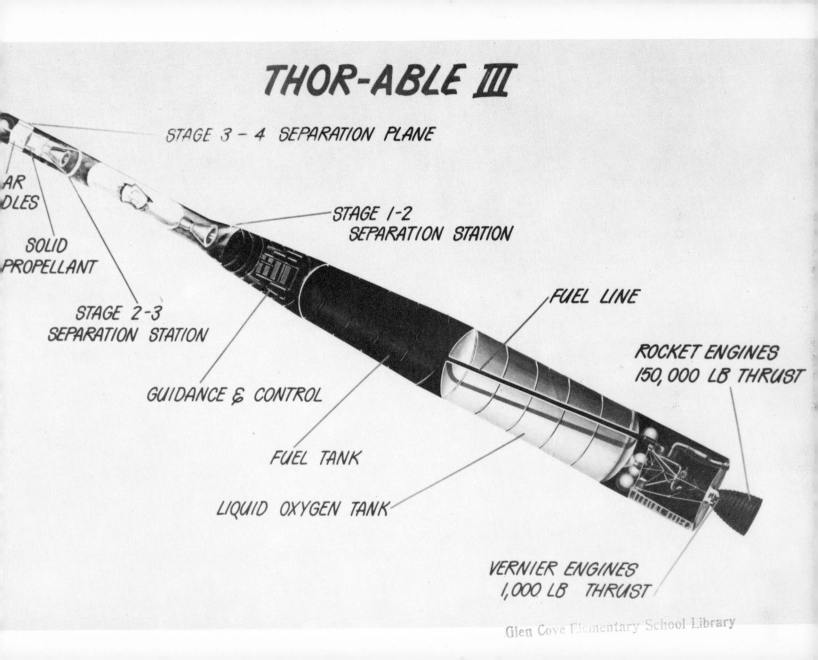

STAGE 3 - 4 SEPARATION PLANE

AR
DLES

SOLID
PROPELLANT

STAGE 1-2
SEPARATION STATION

STAGE 2-3
SEPARATION STATION

FUEL LINE

ROCKET ENGINES
150,000 LB THRUST

GUIDANCE & CONTROL

FUEL TANK

LIQUID OXYGEN TANK

VERNIER ENGINES
1,000 LB THRUST

EXPLORER VI

Explorer VI was placed in orbit successfully, being launched from Cape Canaveral on August 7, 1959, with a three-stage rocket called the Thor-Able III serving as the launching vehicle. The Thor-Able III stands 90 feet high on the pad and weighs 105,000 pounds.

The first stage is an Air Force Thor, intermediate range ballistic missile, minus its guidance system and modified so as to be connected to additional stages. The liquid-fueled Thor propels the vehicle for about 160 seconds after launch. During this period, the roll and pitch of the vehicle is controlled. Upon separation, after burnout, the Thor re-enters the atmosphere and disintegrates.

The second stage fires immediately after the first stage separation. This stage is a liquid-fueled engine and is a modification of earlier Thor-Able rockets, with eight small spin rockets ringed around the outer skin of the stage. This stage two propels the vehicle for about 100 seconds. At second stage burnout, a plastic nose fairing covering the third stage satellite is jettisoned and falls away. At this time also, the eight spin rockets ignite, causing the second and third stages to rotate at 168 revolutions per minute. The payload spins with the remaining stages, thus stabilizing the trajectory of the third stage. About a second and a half after the spin rockets fire, the second stage separtes, falls and burns upon entering the Earth's atmosphere.

The third stage is a solid-propellant rocket which propels the payload to orbital velocity, about 22,000 miles per hour, and ejects it into orbit. It burns for 40 seconds. Just 20 seconds after burnout, while in orbit with the satellite, it is separated by a set of springs, allowing the satellite to continue in orbit alone.

Explorer VI takes about 12½ hours to circle the Earth in its elongated 91,000-mile orbit which carries it 26,440 miles away at apogee (farthest from Earth) and in as close as 156 miles at perigee (closest to Earth).

The body of the satellite is spheriod-shaped, with a slightly flattened bottom. It is 26 inches in diameter and 29 inches deep, and its aluminum skin is 1/16th of an inch thick.

To non-scientific eyes, the most striking feature of this satellite is the solar paddle system. These vanes extend nearly three feet from the payload's aluminum skin. They are made of honeycomb plastic.

Explorer VI Satellite, known popularly as The Paddlewheel. Paddles convert solar energy to electric energy.

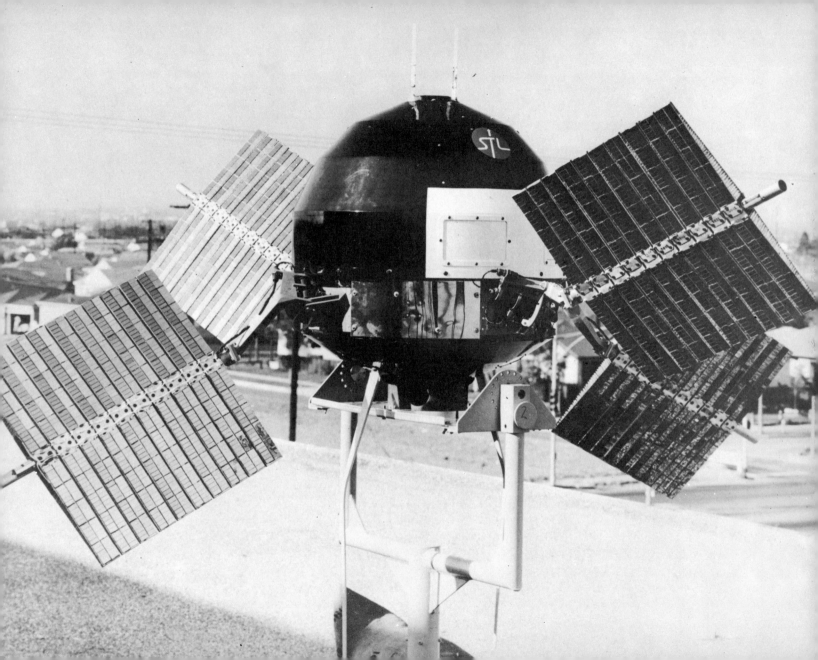

Covering the honeycomb are tiny silicon-based solar cells, lined up in series to generate voltage. A glass filter shields each cell from harmful ultraviolet rays while letting in the proper light. The cell causes a conversion of light energy to electrical energy.

During launch, the paddles, which are mounted on pivotal aluminum arms with springs at the point where they join the satellite, ride folded downward. They spring up and lock into place just before third stage ignition, after the plastic jacket covering the third stage and payload is jettisoned. In flight, the paddles are slightly cocked, so they are exposed to maximum sunlight. These paddles gave the satellite the popular name of "The Paddlewheel."

The 15 major experiments in this 142-pound satellite, together with its advanced electronics, made it the most comprehensive scientific package the United States had put in orbit up to that time.

Most of the experiments ride bolted to a plastic and metal floor within the satellite. They break down in six main categories:

1. Three devices to map the radiation belts ringing the Earth, with each of the instruments concentrating on a specific radiation energy level.

2. A 2½-pound scanning device, something like a TV camera, designed to relay a crude picture of the Earth's cloud cover.

3. Solar cells, 8,000 in all, or 1,000 on each side of the four paddles, to create voltage to recharge the satellite's chemical batteries in flight. The electronic gear in this satellite includes three transmitters and two receivers.

4. A micrometeorite detector, built to gauge the size and speed of meteoric particles hitting the satellite.

5. Two types of magnetometers to map the Earth's magnetic field.

6. Four experiments to study the behavior of radio waves, all aimed at finding out more about deep space communications.

Once a satellite is successfully placed in orbit, it is usually some weeks, and often months, before the data sent back can be completely analyzed and definite conclusions drawn.

Explorer VI was able to contribute much more information about the radiation belts than any of its predecessors, for the simple reason that it made two trips daily through the belts. Data obtained confirms some facts and rouses considerable theory about the structure of the radiation spectrum. Very low energy particles were measured for the first time with a device called a scintillometer.

In the first two days of orbit, Explorer VI was hit by 28 micrometeorites, particles no bigger than a speck of dust. The impact rate indicated the presence of one micrometeorite in a volume about the size of the Empire State Building.

The facsimile device, the TV cameralike affair, sent back signals to give a crude picture of the cloud layer. These signals were recorded on magnetic tape, similar to that used by commercial television stations to record programs off the air for later release.

Solid signals and reception were reported in the radio wave experiments and the two magnetometers successfully sent back readings. This data adds to the present knowledge about the ionosphere and will help scientists to solve the problem of deep space communications which must penetrate this highly energized layer of the atmosphere.

THE INFLATABLE SPHERE SATELLITE

In the search for knowledge of the atmosphere, an unusual type of satellite was designed to meet a specific need.

The Earth's atmosphere, trapped in place by gravity, is heaviest at the surface, thinning out to a virtual vacuum at a farther distance from the planet.

Instrumented balloons first explored the upper atmosphere to heights of 20 miles. Telemetry showed that air density thins out with increasing altitude. Plotted on a graph, air density decreases with altitude in a smooth curve. Early sounding rocket experiments after World War II reinforced these findings.

It was found, however, that, in addition to altitude, air density is affected by at least three other factors: time of day, time of year and solar radiation.

Standard sea level atmosphere at zero degrees Centigrade contains 26,850,000,000,000,000,000 air molecules per cubic centimeter. In 1946, using instrumented balloon measurements, scientists in projected atmospheric density prediciton to altitudes not yet explored by man — warning that there might be an error by a factor of 1,000 at great heights.

Subsequent sounding rocket studies showed that at 110 miles, the number of air molecules per cubic centimeter drops off to 5,810,000,000. New projections on higher altitudes were made, estimated by physicists to be accurate within a factor of four to six.

In October, 1958, computations on the decay of the orbit of Sputnik I showed the upper atmosphere more dense than predicted in the later projection. Air drag studies on later Sputniks, and United States Explorer and Vanguard satellites, show that, at 400 miles altitude, air density is about 6,000,000 molecules per cubic centimeter.

By the way, these molecules have an individual diameter of .00000003 centimeter (three one-hundred-thousandths of a centimeter). If each one could be blown up to the size of a tennis ball, each ball would be more than ten miles from its nearest neighbor at that 400-mile altitude.

To make additional air drag measurements, an inflatable sphere is an ideal instrument because its light weight and comparatively large size make it considerably more sensitive than other satellites to air drag effects.

The only spherical satellites which had been in orbit were Vanguard II and Sputnik I. Other satellites, which are not spheres, present varying frontal areas as they tumble, and are therefore unsuited for air drag measurements.

An experiment using a 12-foot inflatable sphere was scheduled for October 23, 1958, as part of the International Geophysical Year. Fired by a Jupiter-C rocket, the satellite failed to achieve orbit when part of the upper stage cluster, including the payload, separated from the launching vehicle prior to booster burnout.

On January 28, 1959, a 12-foot sphere was launched to a height of 75 miles by a two-stage solid propellant Nike-Cajun rocket, from NASA's Wallops Island Station, Virginia, rocket test facility. The shot successfully demonstrated the ejection and inflation mechanism.

The inflatable sphere weighs about ten pounds and is made of aluminum foil half a mil (half of one-thousands of an inch) thick, sandwiched over a layer of Mylar plastic film a mil thick. The aluminum is highly reflective, to make optical tracking easier, and it provides enough rigidity to maintain the sphere's shape after the inflating nitrogen is bled off into space at orbital height.

The payload consists of a stainless steel cylinder, 7 inches in diameter and 31½ inches long, containing the folded sphere and its ejection and inflation mechanism. Attached to the lower end of the

PAYLOAD SHELL

BEACON ASSEMBLY

INFLATABLE SPHERE

PISTON

BELLOWS

PRESSURE VESSEL

SQUIB-VALVE ASSEMBLY

Below: Inflatable sphere ejecting and inflating procedure. Top left: Inflatable sphere payload. Bottom left: Foil-covered inflatable sphere receives final inspection in factory.

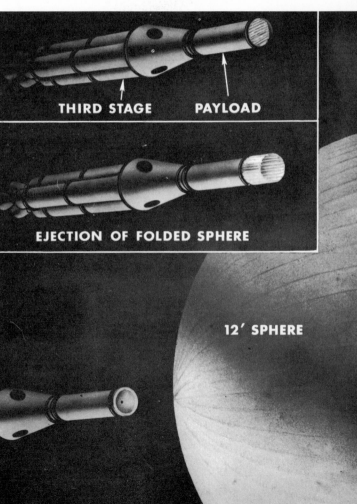

THIRD STAGE   PAYLOAD

EJECTION OF FOLDED SPHERE

12' SPHERE

cylinder is the telemetry assembly, including a transmitter, battery pack and antenna.

Here is the sequence of events in placing the sphere in orbit:

At about eleven minutes after launch, a hydraulic timer completes a circuit which fires two small squibs in the nitrogen pressure vessel. This allows the pressurized nitrogen to expand the bellows, forcing the piston to expel the folded sphere from the cylinder. Ejection and unfolding of the sphere take about 30 seconds. This action takes place after third-stage burnout of the propelling vehicle.

After ejection, nitrogen gas from the bellows passes through a connecting valve and inflates the sphere. This takes 1½ minutes. When the sphere is fully inflated, a spring attached to the stem of the sphere activates and disengages the sphere from the rest of the payload. The time elapsed from ejection into orbit until full separation of the sphere is about four minutes and approximately 15 minutes after launch.

After inflation, the nitrogen is bled off and the sphere retains its shape by the rigidity of the aluminum foil skin.

Following the separation, the sphere and payload will be close neighbors in space and the first tracking fixes on the sphere are made from signals sent out by the transmitter remaining in the payload. Because of the difference in size and weight, however, the sphere and the payload container eventually drift apart as the sphere is affected by the very tenuous gases at orbital height. The drag causes a spiraling orbit which ends in the Earth's denser atmosphere, where the sphere burns up. Through optical tracking, scientists determine how quickly the sphere's orbit decays and calculate air density at the orbital altitudes.

The launching vehicle for the inflatable sphere payload is a modified Juno II, with two solid propellant high energy upper stages. The Juno II stands about 76 feet high and weighs 60 tons, including fuel.

When you consider that a total weight of 84 pounds goes into orbit, including the spent third stage, a comparison between the size of the launching vehicle and the eventual payload reveals one of the basic problems of space exploration.

The Juno II lifts off its pad vertically, tilting into trajectory during the burning time of the first stage. After engine burnout, approximately 3 minutes after launch, explosive bolts separate the booster, which is slowed and steered to one side by four small retrorockets, to prevent interference with the upper stages.

During launch and first stage flight, the upper stage is protected by an aerodynamic shroud which is released by explosive bolts and pushed aside by a lateral rocket. For some 7½ minutes after the booster is separated, the upper stages coast until this aerodynamic shroud is removed.

The second stage then ignites, pulling the upper stage and the payload clear of the shroud. At this time, the payload and third stage are spinning at 600 revolutions per minute, the spin is caused by the action of electric motors which start right after lift off. The spin is to produce stabilization.

The second stage burns for 6 seconds, followed by a coasting period of 2 seconds. The third stage then ignites, burning for an effective time of 6 seconds.

So, 11 minutes after launching, the timer begins the process of releasing and inflating the sphere and, a little more than 5 minutes later, another extension of man's mind is in space.

On Friday, March 11, 1960, one of the most successful and significant advances in the exploration of space was accomplished when a multistage Thor-Able rocket lifted off the launch pad at Cape Canaveral and placed a 90-pound, 26-inch payload into an orbital path that would take it around the sun. Three hours after the launch, NASA scientists in Washington announced the 165,000-pound thrust had given the satellite enough speed to establish an orbit which would take it 74,700,000 miles from the sun at its nearest approach. The satellite was the Pioneer V.

Pioneer V is a paddle-wheel satellite quite similar to the one described earlier. In a matter of days, Pioneer V's radio transmitter had already set a new distance record for radio transmission, reporting back loud and clear from over 2,000,000 miles out in space. It was estimated it would take 311 days for Pioneer V to make a complete circle around the sun.

Pioneer V went to work immediately, relaying data collected by its instruments and devices aboard. The data concerns radiation, the magnetic field, micrometeorite particles and radio propagation. Pioneer V has two transmitters, the first a 5-watt transmitter which was used in the early days of the orbit, and a 150-watt transmitter which took over the job from its smaller brother when the probe was from three-to-five million miles into space.

Pioneer V, planned to come within about seven million miles from the orbit of Venus, is the first artificial satellite with an orbital path entirely between the Earth's orbit and the sun.

Pioneer V remains a tribute to the ability of American scientists and an indication of things to come as the search for knowledge continues.

6 / SUMMARY OF UNITED STATES SPACE PROGRAM

Slowly, as is the custom in democratic processes, our national space program is working toward a more efficient pattern, with sincere attempts being made to weed out duplications of effort, contradiction of purpose and the impedient forces of bureaucracy.

To understand how such undesirable factors might develop in the space program, one has but to examine the top-level organizational structure which existed in the waning months of 1959.

The President of the United States and Commander-in-Chief of the Armed Forces had a Special Assistant for Science and Technology whose responsibility was to advise the President on all matters pertaining to the space program and all other technological affairs in the nation.

Also reporting to the President and assisting in the formulation of policy and the making of decisions was the National Aeronautics and Space Council.

One step down the organizational ladder came the National Aeronautics and Space Administration (NASA), a very competent organization which is an outgrowth of the former National Advisory Council for Aeronautics (NACA), the group most responsible for all of our progress in aviation, both military and civilian.

Next in line of direct authority was the Secretary of Defense. Between the NASA and the Secretary of Defense was a coordinating body called the Civilian-Military Liaison Committee.

The Secretary of Defense had a Director of Research and Engineering and the Advanced Research Projects Agency (ARPA).

Next came the Secretaries of the three military departments with their civilian and military assistants aiding in the direction of research and development, production and operational uses of space age products.

With the three military services engaged in their own specific projects, working jointly with each other, with industry and both the NASA and ARPA, as well as universities and research foundations, it is understandable that the line of authority and control might sometimes be lost in the maze.

Slowly but surely, we are moving toward a more concentrated program for the conquest and utilization of space.

In a general recapitulation, considering the activities of the National Aeronautics and Space Administration (NASA), the Department of Defense's Advanced Research Projects Agency (ARPA), industry, universities, research foundations and the three military services, the United States space program includes these projects:

X-15 Program — Manned experimental rocket-powered aircraft, intended to carry man to altitudes of 100 miles or more at speeds in excess of 3,600 miles per hour, with a power-off landing being made back to Earth. Joint effort of NASA, Air Force, Navy and North American Aviation, manufacturer of the three test vehicles.

Dyna-Soar Program — This is the next step beyond the X-15 program and will lead to development of an orbital reconnaissance patrol bomber. Progressing toward this goal, the vehicle will be launched in mid-air in the same manner in which the X-15 is launched from a B-52. It will attain near-orbital speed, then skip and glide in and out of the atmosphere and eventually glide back to home base, using aerodynamic controls. Primarily a project of the Air Force and industry.

Project Mercury — A program of pilot training and vehicle development, leading to manned orbital flight up to 150 miles into space, with a manned capsule being launched into controlled orbit by a modified Atlas. Short range training flights to be launched by Redstone missile. NASA project, with aeromedical assistance from Air Force, Navy, univertities and industry. Capsule manufactured by McDonnell Aircraft Corporation.

Project Discoverer — Purpose of this program is to learn methods of stabilization for space craft, to explore systems of escape from capsules and to gather biological data. It will also test methods of capsule recovery. Polar-orbiting satellites launched Thor-Able rockets from Vandenburg Air Force Base, California. Later launching in the series by Atlas rocket. Findings to give support to Project Mercury and Dyna-Soar program. Directed by ARPA, with launchings by the Ballistic Missiles Division of the Air Force.

Project Mrs. V — Taking data from Project Discoverer, with supply studies on controllable and recoverable satellites. An ARPA project.

Project Transit — The objective of this project is to conduct research toward the development of navigational satellites which can guide airplanes and ships through signals delivered by space vehicles. Data would also contribute to eventual space navigational system for space vehicles. Instrumentation used to be developed by the United States Navy Bureau of Ordnance, with propulsion and launching equipment developed by the USAF Air Research and Development Command and Ballistic Missiles Division.

Project Samos — This is a continuation of the project previously named Pied Piper and would work toward the development of an advanced reconnaissance polar-orbiting satellite system. Data from Project Discoverer will assist this project, a joint effort of USAF Ballistic Missiles Division and Lockheed Aircraft.

Project Courier — A continuation of the earlier Project Score which put an Atlas missile in orbit, with transmitting, receiving and recording equipment, permitting exchange of communications between Earth and the satellite. Courier to be a message storer communications satellite, using a delayed repeater system. Experimental vehicles to be launched into 300- to 500-mile orbits. The Army Signal Corps is to plan satellite and ground communications equipment, with USAF Ballistic Missiles Division providing launching device.

Project Defender — Sponsored by the ARPA and using the facilities of all three military services, this project is an effort to gather sufficient data to develop an anti-missile defense system, Project represents more than fifty studies in several areas.

Project Midas — This is a research and development program, with the objective of developing a satellite early warning system against ballistic missiles, using infrared and other techniques. Sponsored by ARPA, Air Force Ballistic Missiles Division has sole responsibility for project.

Project Orion — A feasibility study of advanced types of rocket propulsion, to be condubted by the General Atomic Division of the General Dynamics Corporation. ARPA-sponsored, with contracts let by USAF Air Research and Development Command.

Project Principia — A study of solid-fuel propellants under over fifty ARPA contracts, with all three military services taking part.

Project Tiros — An NASA-sponsored program of research and development studies, leading to a 250-pound meteorological satellite, equipped with two television cameras and two infrared detectors.

There are several projects in the essential area of propellants, both liquid and solid. Some of these projects are continuations of present launching systems, with new modification and improvements being made, while others are fresh advances in the field of propulsion. The main projects are these:

Thor-Able — An Air Force project assigned by ARPA. Thor-Able is a four-stage carrier for space probes. First stage is USAF Thor, second stage is Vanguard, third stage an Alleghany Ballistics Laboratory solid-fuel rocket and the fourth stage a Thiokol solid-fuel rocket. Thor-Able was used for Pioneer I lunar probe and may be used to deliver a small payload to the vicinity of Venus.

Thor-Hustler — This has a Thor first stage and a Bell Hustler second stage. It has been used as the carrier for the ARPA-USAF Discoverer series. In some applications, the Atlas may be use in place of the Thor.

Juno IV — An Army development for NASA, with possible Mars and Venus mission. Jupiter first stage. Vanguard first stage used as second stage, plus Vanguard third stage used as third stage.

Vanguard — A three-stage vehicle, developed by the Navy for NASA, manufactured by the Martin Company. First stage is Vanguard GE liquid-fuel rocket, second stage an Aerojet General liquid-fuel rocket and the third stage a solid-fuel rocket, built by Grand Central Rocket.

Scout — A four-stage, solid-propellant vehicle, developed by NASA. Capable of putting a 150-pound payload into a 300-mile orbit or 100 pounds to over 5,000-mile orbit. Payload test flights from NASA Test Facility at Wallops Island, Virginia. First stage is an Aerojet-General modified Polaris engine, second stage a Thiokol improved Sergeant rocket, third and fourth stages are Alleghany Ballistic Laboratory rockets.

Little Joe — A cluster of four Sergeant solid-fuel engines, assembled by the Army Ballistic Missile Agency for NASA. NASA test vehicle used in Mercury Project.

Atlas-Able — A four-stage vehicle which could carry a 300-pound payload into a Venusian orbit. It is developed by the Air Force for NASA. The Atlas-Able first stage can be combined with other vehicles, for example, the Atlas-Hustler, Centaur, Vega and others, for a variety of missions.

Atlas-Hustler — Used in the USAF-ARPA Discoverer series. It is a follow-on of Thor-Hustler, with Atlas replacing Thor in combination with the Bell Hustler. Can put 3,000 pounds into a 300-mile orbit.

Centaur — Atlas first stage, with Pratt & Whitney Aircraft upper stage using oxygen-hydrogen fuel.

An NASA vehicle capable of placing 8,000-pound payloads into 300-mile orbit. Combined with Vega as third stage, it could send a two-ton payload to the Moon.

Delta — Developed by Douglas Aircraft for NASA. A three-stage vehicle to place 250 pounds in a 300-mile orbit or 100 pounds in a deep space probe mission. First stage is a modified Thor. The second stage is an Aerojet-General rocket with radio-inertial guidance, and the third stage is a solid-fuel Alleghany Ballistics Laboratory rocket. First two stages are liquid-fuel. This vehicle has about 150,000 pounds' thrust and it is in interim use while larger vehicles are devloped.

Nova — An NASA developmental project, clustering four F-1 North American Rocketdyne engines as booster. With upper stages, it is expected to be capable of placing a 200,000-pound payload into a 300-mile orbit, of making a manned landing on the Moon and propelling a controllable satellite.

Saturn — Originally an ARPA program to develop a 1,500,000-pound engine cluster, using Thor, Atlas and Jupiter missiles. An Army Ordnance Missile Command contract with North American Rocketdyne. The second stage is a modified Titan booster. Third and fourth stages are rockets using oxygen-hydrogen combination fuel and the fifth stage using storable liquid fuel.

Vega — An NASA project for a three-stage vehicle that can place a two-ton space laboratory into a 300-mile orbit for several weeks. Modified Atlas first stage, second stage using a Vanguard booster. By adding a third-stage Jet Propulsion Laboratory vehicle, fueled by storable liquids, could place a 1,000-pound payload in the vicinity of the Moon or a slightly lighter payload could be sent on interplanetary missions. Convair Division of General Dynamics Corporation is the prime contractor. Schedule called for delivery of eight vehicles by late 1961, after flight tests in 1960.

Those are the highlights of the United States space program. It is an impressive program. If these objectives can be translated into reality, perhaps we will have gained a parity with the Russians, maybe we will even surpass them. The greatest danger to the attainment of this goal is not scientific progress by the Soviets . . . *but American indifference.*

Our scientists need behind them the full weight of American public opinion, welded in a unity of purpose, with a sincere desire to compete and excel. Without this kind of support, our chances in the race for control of space are doubtful.

The constant pressure of a militant and aggressive Communism keeps emphasis on the purely military aspects of the space program. Because of the acute need for a reliable means of detecting enemy missiles and having a method of defending ourselves against them, vital importance is attached to such projects as Midas. This project will give us an orbiting infrared sensor which will allow up to thirty minutes of warning of the approach of an enemy missile. The effectiveness of our retaliatory strength, both manned bombers and ballistic missiles, is almost guaranteed by the warning capability of Midas. We must buy time because the element most essential to our security is just that . . . *time*.

After Midas, the follow-up project which will further augment our deterrent power is Project Samos. The Samos satellite will let us look inside any country and detect even the preparations for a hostile attack. This will give us even more time to implement our deterrent force of manned bombers and ballistic missiles.

As a development companion of Midas and Samos, Project Defender is working toward allowing us the capability to destroy incoming missiles with missiles.

While these projects are under way, a new kind of race has developed between our Strategic Air Command and the manned strategic forces of the Russians. This is the predicted race to produce an operational air-launched ballistic missile, or ALBM, using conventional manned bombers as the launching pad, with such missiles having a range of as much as 1500 miles from the point of launch.

The United States version of the ALBM is called the Sky Bolt. It is a two-stage, solid-propellant missile, developed by the Douglas Aircraft Company. Carrying a nuclear warhead, the Sky Bolt is designed for launching from altitudes up to 45,000 feet, with the launch taking place at speeds around 600 miles per hour. After launch, the Sky Bolt takes up a ballistic trajectory which carries it as much as 300 miles out of the atmosphere while it develops a speed of approximately 5,000 miles per hour, with yet a higher speed being attained as it makes a re-entry of the atmosphere and heads for the target area.

The Sky Bolt is planned for use by the Boeing B-52G and B-52H jet bombers. These manned bombers now carry a shorter range air-to-ground missile called the Hound Dog. When a nuclear-powered bomber is realized, there is a probability that the Sky Bolt, or an improved successor, will be used by the new bomber.

The development of the Sky Bolt adds greatly to the present deterrent power of the Strategic Air Command and buys us more of the vital time element we may desperately need to close the so-called missile gap.

However, to point up the seriousness of the situation, it is known that the Russians also have a development program under way for an ALBM. The Russian ALBM is said to be planned for use by the Bear turboprop bomber and by the Bounder supersonic delta-winged bomber, some versions of which will be nuclear-powered.

The ALBM race illustrates the complexities of the space age. While we strive to gain knowledge and move into the utilization and possible control of space, we must also keep our feet on the ground and continually improve our ability to deter an enemy from making an attack on us.

With the growing understanding of the challenge of the space age, there is every indication that America will meet the challenge courageously, moving toward the use of space for the benefit of all mankind, while maintaining the military strength to deter aggression against the Free World.

7 / YOU AND SPACE

The Average American does not want to take a trip into space. He probably knows no one who does. But, for the person who will never be an astronaut, a space vehicle pilot, or even a space traveler, the space program will have special benefits to offer him, in fact, some of them are already here.

By developing a military capability in space, the average American is assured safety from aggression, preservation of our way of life and the retention of our prestige among nations.

There are other personal, individual and intimate benefits to be derived from the space program.

In order to place a man in space, science must create for him an artificial environment. To know exactly what this environment must be, studies had to be made to determine the ability of the human body and mind to withstand the demands of space flight. These human factors studies, as they are called, constituted the most intensive investigation of the physiological and psychological capabilities of the human being ever undertaken.

As a segment of this study program, scores of volunteers, the X-15 pilots and the astronauts in their training programs have been subjected to stresses the average person will never experience. Every facet of the functioning of the body and mind has been explored.

The human factors program has produced new knowledge and developed new methods and equipment for the study of the human being. The knowledge thus gained contributes in many ways to giving ordinary people a better chance for a healthier, happier and longer life.

Many of the devices and instruments developed in the human factors program are already being incorporated into the everyday routine of the medical profession.

As an example, the process of diagnosis is being greatly speeded up by such things as transducers, little metal discs which perform much the same as a microphone which picks up audible sound and transposes it into electronic energy. The electronic impulses are then fed through an amplifier and reconverted into audible sound. A small disc, strapped to the chest, can fill an auditorium with amplified sound of a beating heart. Similar devices can report instantaneously on the functioning of the nervous system, the respiratory system and the entire circulatory system.

A touch thermometer is another development. By touching the tip to any part of the body, the temperature is instantly revealed.

A probing tube may be inserted along the major arteries, right into the heart itself, for close scrutiny of a trouble spot.

These are just a few from among the countless devices finding their way from the space program into everyday medical use. Because of the work of aeromedics, many of us will be around longer to enjoy being healthy.

The medical profession is but one of many fields that are already receiving benefits from the exploration of space. The demand for new and better techniques, processes, metals, materials, fabrics and fuels creates a stimulus for science and industry. For practically every kind of progress made for the space program, there is some application to general civilian use.

Many features of your new automobile, the cigarette-pack-size transistor radios, your portable television sets, the gadget that lets you stay in the ease of your favorite chair while you switch channels and control the volume of your TV set, the clothing you wear, the machines that do computations and calculations for you, answer the phone and record the message — all these and hundreds of others are directly due to the impetus of the space program.

In a more general sense, there are at least three specific uses of satellites which will eventually contribute to the well-being of every individual.

The potentialities of the *communications satellite* open the door for such advances as world-wide television, around-the-globe radio-telephones and facsimile mail that will instantly deliver a message anywhere in your handwriting.

Basically, the communications satellite is a relay station for signals originating from one point and being directed to another point on Earth.

The ideal situation makes use of what is called a 24-hour satellite. It is placed in orbit in such a manner that it will make one orbital revolution every 24 hours. The orbital path must be perfectly circular, and the satellite must be launched directly over the Equator, with its path remaining in the equatorial plane. The altitude should be precisely 22,000 miles. While the ideal situation cannot be accomplished, it can be approached near enough for the satellite to move with relative slowness over a definite portion of the Earth's surface. This permits ground stations to maintain reasonable contact with it.

One satellite of this type will be within sight of nearly one-half of the Earth's surface. With three of them correctly placed, virtually complete global coverage at all times is accomplished.

Lower orbit satellites can also be used as communications relay stations but they would have corresponding disadvantages. They would give line of sight coverage to a smaller area of Earth and they would be moving much faster in relation to the Earth, making continuous contact with them more difficult.

There are two types of communications satellites, active and passive.

An *active* satellite has equipment aboard with which it receives a signal from the Earth, amplifies it and rebroadcasts the same signal back to Earth, either immediately or after a delay. The Score Satellite was an example of an active communications satellite. You may recall that President Dwight D. Eisenhower broadcast a Christmas message to the Score in 1958, and the message was then rebroadcast back to Earth.

A *passive* communications satellite is one which merely reflects or scatters the signal it receives, returning the signal back to Earth by reflection. This is similar to the ionosphere scatter system but using a man-made satellite rather than an atmospheric layer to accomplish the reflection.

The inflatable sphere satellite described earlier is an example of the type of satellite that might be used for communications.

A much larger version of the inflatable sphere described caused near panic on the Eastern seaboard in late October, 1959. Without advance warning, an inflatable sphere roughly as high as a four-story building was released in an NASA experiment from Wallops Island, Virginia. Switchboards of military installations, law enforcement agencies, radio and television stations, newspapers and Civil Defense were flooded with frantic reports of the huge object. With an explanation from the NASA came sighs of relief and marveling at the age in which we live!

The individual probably will never be aware of it but anyone who travels long distances, either by high-speed aircraft or ocean-going ships, will derive benefits from *navigational satellites*.

Satellites will provide the basis for an all-weather navigational system which will give the accurate geodetic position, speed and direction of aircraft and surface vessels.

83

Navigational satellites may be used in two ways:

Sphereographical — This is a system very similar to celestial navigational methods, but instead of measuring the angle between the vertical and two stars, the same method is used to measure two successive positions of the satellite, the speed and orbital direction of which is known. Because of the speed of the satellite, this is a difficult method.

A sphereographical satellite also radiates a continuous radio signal. With an electronic sextant and vertical indicator, an observer can determine his position by two successive radio readings of the satellite.

Doppler-shift method — This method is based upon the phenomenon that a radio signal from a passing vehicle, in this case a navigational satellite, seems to be higher in frequency as the vehicle approaches the observer, and lower in frequency as it moves away from the observer. When a constant radio signal is measured with the proper equipment, and a comparison is made with the known frequency of the signal and the observed frequency, data is provided on the relative position of the vehicle and the observer. The local vertical does not need to be known in this method.

Because the method is dependent upon frequency variation measurements, an essential requirement is that the satellite carry a radio transmitter with a very stable frequency.

Navigational satellites offer us a greater ability to move rapidly from one point on Earth to another without getting lost.

Probably each of us is a weatherman of sorts. In spite of the best prognostications of our professional meteorologists, we still make knowing guesses at the weather ourselves, if not audibly, at least in the back of our minds. Now, both we and the professionals will get a needed assist from *weather satellites*.

Weather satellites, placed in orbit above the cloud cover and carrying miniature vidicon television cameras, offer a view of the world-wide cloud pattern not possible with the ground observation system.

In the initial stages of development, this added dimension of observation, plus the fact that it would cover areas over large oceans and other remote places which cannot now be observed from Earth, will add tremendously to the reliability of weather forecasting.

As the method develops, wind directions and temperatures can be estimated from this below and above observation through study of known characteristics of cloud formations. Later, infrared and other electromagnetic devices can be employed in satellites to investigate weather conditions around the globe.

Through a new source of observation and weather conditions investigation, more accurate forecasting will work to the benefit of everyone.

Another growing dream of man is the control of the weather. At the present time, this accomplishment is not in the foreseeable future. However, we cannot say such control is not possible. In the years to come, as we gather more accurate and thorough knowledge of the Earth's atmosphere and the causes of various storm phenomena, we may find ways to exert an influence on the type of weather we are to have in a given area.

With the real barrier to progress existing primarily in the minds of men, knowledge and understanding will make possible advances we may never have dreamed of so far.

For those of you who *do* want to be astronauts and space pilots, here are some sample questions that were used to gauge the ability and evaluate the personality of the volunteers who wanted to be selected as Project Mercury astronauts.

These questions were prepared by the Psychological Corporation of New York which furnished a number of the written tests used in the Mercury astronaut selection program.

In the ability test sampling, the correct answers will be found on page 93. The personality questions, however, have no correct answers. The responses help the psychologist in making a personal evaluation.

The first two sets of questions are similar to those in the Miller Analogies Test and the Minnesota Engineering Analogies Test.

Directions: Look at the first analogy item below. You read it thus: LIGHT is to DARK as PLEASURE is to ?. The correct answer among the four choices is *pain,* so *c* has been underscored at the right. In each test item, find the word which completes the analogy and underline its letter (a, b, c, or d) at the right.

LIGHT : DARK : : PLEASURE : (a. picnic, b. day, c. pain, d. night)   a b <u>c</u> d

1. LAUGH : (a. joke, b. cry, c. grin, d. humor) : : JOY : SORROW   a <u>b</u> c d

2. RECOVER : (a. bottle, b. correct, c. rescind, d. renew) : : RECOUP : RECTIFY   a b <u>c</u> d

3. FICTION : (a. memory, b. fact, c. novel, d. imagination) : : AUTOBIOGRAPHY : RECALL   a b <u>c</u> d

4. REDUNDANT : REPETITIOUS : : (a. non sequitor, b. false premise, c. recurrence, d. precondition) : FALSE CONCLUSION   a <u>b</u> c d

MINNESOTA ENGINEERING ANALOGIES TEST

1. BRASS : ALLOY : : IRON : (a. compound, b. element, c. steel, d. rust)   a b c d

2. CONDUCTANCE : RESISTANCE : : MULTIPLY : (a. integrate, b. magnify, c. divide, d. differentiate)   a b c d

3. BODY : PHYSIOLOGY : : TRIANGLE : (a. astronomy, b. algebra, c. calculus, d. trigonometry)   a b c d

4. VACUUM TUBE : THYRATRON : : CONTINUOUS : (a. alternating, b. regular, c. discrete, d. diminishing)   a b c d

Directions: Each problem in this test consists of five mathematical figures or expressions. Four of these have something in common which is not shared by the remaining one. You are to choose the *one* figure or expression which does *not* belong with the other four and show your choice by underlining it.

1.	2.	3.	4.
(A) 15	(A) circle	(A) 7:49	(A) $x + y = 12$
(B) 25	(B) ellipse	(B) 6:36	(B) $2y = 2x + 5$
(C) 125	(C) parabola	(C) 5:25	(C) $3y = 7 - 3x$
(D) 317	(D) square	(D) 4:16	(D) $5y + 5x = 9$
(E) 625	(E) triangle	(E) 3:12	(E) $4x = 5 - 4y$

Directions: Personality Inventory. Read each statement and mark whether it is true or false as applied to you. If a statement does not apply to you, omit it. Try to mark each item.

	True	False
1. I often worry about my health.	True_____	False_____
2. I am often unhappy.	True_____	False_____
3. Sometimes I feel like cursing.	True___✓___	False_____
4. Strangers keep trying to hurt me.	True_____	False_____

INCOMPLETE SENTENCES

Directions: Complete these sentences to express your real feelings. Be sure to make a complete sentence.

1. I am sorry that ....
2. I can never ....
3. I hope ....
4. At times ....

Now let us pretend you are not an astronaut but the pilot of the X-15. How do you prepare for a flight? Well, here is the procedure:

X-15 COUNTDOWN PROCEDURES

PRIOR TO FLIGHT DAY
1. Flight briefing
2. Premating inspection, including systems checkout
3. Mate B-52/X-15

FLIGHT DAY (24-hour countdown)
1. Service X-15 pilot's suit vent nitrogen.
2. X-15 pilot's oxygen servicing
3. B-52 pneumatic system servicing
4. B-52 nitrogen topoff
5. Service X-15 APU (hydrogen peroxide and helium)
6. Service X-15 liquid nitrogen system

7. Fill X-15 helium system
8. X-15 water/alcohol/nitrogen servicing
9. Service liquid oxygen, nitrogen control, propellant helium system
10. Final briefing, X-15, pilot, B-52 crew
11. B-52 crew boards airplane
12. X-15 pilot boards airplane
13. Close and lock canopy
14. Tow B-52/X-15 to engine start area
15. Chase pilots man airplanes
16. Start B-52 engines
17. B-52 cockpit check

18. X-15 cockpit check
19. B-52 taxies to runway for takeoff
20. Chase airplane takeoff
21. B-52/X-15 takeoff
22. Climb to 38,000 feet

X-15 PILOT
23. 12-minute warning
   Data burst
   Gage readings
   Windshield nitrogen OFF
24. 8-minute warning
   Ram air closed
   Pressurization cooling OFF
   Blowers ON
   Jettison switches OFF

87

25. 7-minute warning
    Nitrogen bleed ON
    Chamber pressure check
    Governor balance check
    Check preheat ON
    Data burst
26. 6-minute warning
    Tank handle to PRESSURIZE
    Data ON and calibrate
27. 5-minute warning
    APU's ON
    Reset generators
    Reset SAS
    Set SAS gains
    Hydraulic pressure check
    Electrical power check
28. 4-minute warning
    Tank handle to JETTISON
    Liquid oxygen jettison check
    Water/alcohol and peroxide
    jettison check
    Tank handle to PRESSURIZE
    Data OFF
    Data ON
29. 3-minute warning
    Control motion rudder, lateral and SAS check
    Data OFF
    Select X-15 oxygen
    Launch light ON
    Power OFF
    Data ON
30. 1-minute warning
    Engine master switch ON
    Prime switches ON
    Fast-slave gyro
    Arm ventral jettison
    Final OK

B-52 PILOT
31. Move master arming switch ON, begin radio countdown, 5-4-3-2-1, drop (at drop, turn launch switch ON)

X-15 PILOT
32. Recovery
    Start engine

That's it! You're now on your own.

All you have to do now is fly your mission.

During the 88-second burnout period of your XLR-99 engine, you should attain a speed of approximately 3,600 miles per hour. Climb to an altitude of about 500,000 feet. On leaving aerodynamic control area, test ballistic attitude control rockets in space flight. Begin your descent. After passing 115,000 feet altitude, begin your recovery procedure. You will take about 7.33 G's during the pullout. Make constant check of all gauges and instruments. Keep voice contact with ground control. On entering glide pattern, make contact with chase planes. Let them help you with airspeed and altitude checks on final approach to Edwards.

Set her down easy on the steel skids. She only weighs a little over 13,000 pounds now, including you. You used about 8½ tons of fuel on the way up. Keep her straight when that nose wheel slams down and ride her out.

Well, that was a fine job, well done! Now, just one more thing.

Take it easy on the drive home from the base. Those California highways are murder!

ANSWERS TO TESTS ON PAGES 85, 86

1. b	1. b	1. (D)
2. b	2. c	2. (C)
3. d	3. d	3. (E)
4. a	4. c	4. (B)

8 / ORBITAL FLIGHT PATHS

The basic types of paths in space flight are determined by the gravitational attraction properties of concentrated masses of material and Newton's Laws of Motion.

The path to be taken by a vehicle or satellite can be estimated by the known velocity it will attain. To direct a vehicle into a certain path, propulsion devices must be so used as to give it a specific velocity. If there is variation in the velocity reached, the eventual path of the vehicle will vary from that intended.

The dividing line between "local" and "long-distant" flight in space is a speed called *escape velocity*.

The speed required to place a satellite in orbit a few hundred miles above the Earth is about 25,000 feet per second. This is called *orbital speed* and results in an elliptical orbital path being followed continuously around the Earth for a period of time depending upon the altitude and type of vehicle.

Escape velocity for the Earth is about 36,700 feet per second. Vehicles reaching, or exceeding, this speed take up an open-end parabolic path and thus move into interplanetary space. Vehicles at velocities greater than escape velocity enter an open-end hyperbolic path and can make deep space penetration.

If the mass of a planet and its surface gravity are known, it is then possible to calculate the escape velocity. Thus the following table:

| PLANET | VELOCITIES IN FEET PER SECOND | | TIME OF |
	Escape velocity from planet listed	Minimum launching velocity from Earth to reach planet listed	TRAVEL FROM EARTH
Mercury	13,600	44,000	110 days
Venus	33,600	38,000	150 days
Earth	36,700		
Moon	7,800	36,700*	2½ days
Mars	16,700	38,000	200 days
Jupiter	197,000	46,000	2.7 years
Saturn **		49,000	6 years
Uranus **		51,000	16 years
Neptune **		52,000	31 years
Pluto *		53,000	46 years
From entire solar system	54,000		

*The gravitational field of the Moon gives some assistance for an Earth-to-Moon flight but it is so slight the reduction is minor from Earth escape velocity.

**Surface gravity, one of the requirements for calculating escape velocity, is not known for Giant Planets, thus there are no figures for them.

GLOSSARY

AEROMEDICAL — Pertaining to the practice of aviation medicine.

ASTROMEDICAL — Pertaining to medical studies and practices connected with man's environment in space.

ASTRONOMY — The study of celestial bodies and their movement in the universe.

BALLISTIC CONTROL ROCKETS — A unique feature of the X-15 rocket-powered experimental aircraft. Eight hydrogen-peroxide-fueled jet nozzles in the nose and four in the wings produce enough thrust to allow the pilot to control the attitude of the vehicle during ballistic trajectory outside the atmosphere.

BEACON — A device carried in a satellite or sounding rocket to send out a constant or intermittent radio signal as an aid to tracking.

BOOSTER — The propellant vehicle used to boost a vehicle off the launching pad. Often the first stage is called a booster or the term may be applied to additional smaller rockets which initially aid the first stage in lift-off.

CELESTIAL NAVIGATION — A means of determining a position on the Earth by measuring the angle formed with the absolute vertical and a line leading to two or more stars or other celestial bodies. The oldest form of navigation, used for centuries by ships.

CENTRIFUGE — A machine for inducting artificial gravity by means of centrifugal forces, used in testing the ability of flying personnel to withstand above-normal gravitational forces.

ELLIPTICAL — Pertaining to an ellipse, a flattened or oblongated circle. The orbital path of the Earth is an ellipse.

ENVIRONMENT — The aggregate of all external and internal conditions. In space terminology, artificially created conditions under which man can exist in space.

ESCAPE VELOCITY — The speed which is required for a vehicle to escape from the gravitational forces of the planet from which it is being launched. In the case of the Earth, escape velocity is 36,700 feet per second.

G FORCES — A unit of measurement of the gravitational forces as applied to the pressures exerted upon flying personnel during acceleration and deceleration. A G force is the unit by which the weight of a person or body will be increased by gravity while in movement.

HYPERBOLIC — In Space terminology, an open-ended plane curve which leads off into infinity. The path taken by a vehicle launched at a speed greater than escape velocity.

LIGHTHOUR — A unit of astronomical distance. The distance that can be traveled by an object in one hour at the speed of light, or 186,000 miles per second.

LIGHTYEAR — Distance traveled in one year at the speed of light.

LOGISTICS — A term applied to all activities concerning the support of a vehicle, project, mission or operation of any sort. It includes supplies, repairs, replacement of parts, maintenance, rations and all other activities connected with continuing an operation.

LOX — Common term for liquid oxygen.

MATING — Placing together, as the X-15 is mated to the B-52.

ORBITAL VELOCITY — Speed required to place a satellite in orbit. In the case of the Earth, orbital speed is about 25,000 feet per second.

PARABOLICAL — Path taken by a vehicle launched at escape velocity. An open-ended plane curve of lesser arc than a hyperbolic curve. Not being a closed orbit, it leads into infinity.

PAYLOAD — The total load carried into space for a specific purpose as differentiated from the propulsion unit which carries it.

RADAR TELESCOPE — A telescope using high-frequency radio waves as an aid to tracking an object.

SPECTROSCOPE — Instrument for determining the properties of an element. Through the use of prisms, it analyzes light reflected from the element and, by their position on the color spectrum, identifies the element's component.

TELEMETRY — The system by which data is collected and transmitted back from satellites and rockets. Also used in testing of ballistic missiles and experimental aircraft.

TOPOFF — To complete the filling of fuel tanks.

TRANSPONDER — Same as "beacon." Device to send out radio signals.

WEIGHTLESSNESS — State of zero-gravity. Gravitational forces have zero effect.

INDEX

Able, 30
Aeromedics, 82
Air Force Association, 54
Almagest, 5
Alpha Centauri, 13
Armstrong, Neil A., 30
Astroids, 12
Astronauts, 44
Astronaut Training, 50-52
Astronomy, 5
Atlas, 40
Atlas-Able, 77
Atlas Blockhouse, 51
Atlas-Hustler, 77

Baker, 30
Bell X-2, 15

Carpenter, Jr., Lt., Malcolm S., 44-46
Centaur, 77-78
Civilian-Military Liaison Council, 74
Comets, 12
Convair Division, 40
Cooper, Jr., Capt., Leroy G., 46

Copernicus, 5-7
Crossfield, Scott A., 28-29

Delta, 78
Discoverer, 75
Dole, S. H., 10-11
Dyna-Soar, 24, 75

Ericke, Krafft A., 54
Escape velocity, 90
Exosphere, 18
Explorer, 18-19, 64, 68-69

Glenn, Jr., Lt. Col., John H., 48
Grissom, Virgil I., 44

Hipparchus, 5
Human Factors, 28, 30-32

Inflatable sphere, 70-73
Ion-propelled vehicle, 58
Ionosphere, 16-18, 62
Ionosphere scatter, 58

Juno II, 64, 72-73
Juno IV, 77

Jupiter, 5, 11-12
Jupiter C, 70

Kincheloe, Jr., Capt., Iven C., 15-16, 26, 28

Little Joe, 77
Los Alamos Scientific Laboratories, 38
Lunik III, 8

Mars, 5, 11
Martians, 11
McKay, John B., 28
Mercury, 5, 10
Mercury Capsule, 40
Mercury, Project, 40, 75
Mesosphere, 16
Meteorite, 13
Micrometeorites, 13
Moon, 5, 8, 12
Mrs. V., Project, 75

NACA, 74
NASA, 15, 26, 29
Naval Research Laboratories, 9

Neptune, 11
Nike-Asp, 9
North American Aviation, 26
Nova, 78

Paddle Wheel Satellite, 68
Petersen, Lt. Com., Forrest S., 30
Pioneer, 19, 63-64
Pluto, 12
Project Mercury, 38-40, 75
Proxima Centauri, 13
Ptolemy, 5

Radiation belts, 18-19
Reaction Motors, 34
Rushworth, Capt., Robert A., 29

Samos, Project, 76
Saturn, 5, 11

Saturn, Project, 78
Schirra, Jr., Lt. Com., Walter M., 48
Score, Project, 63, 76
Scout, 77
Shepard, Jr., Alan B., 46-48
Slayton, Capt., Donald K., 46
Solar energy vehicle, 58-60
Space liner, 54
Space shuttle ship, 54-56
Spectroscope, 9
Sputnik I, 70
Stratosphere, 16
Study program, USAF, 21
Sun, 5, 9

Thermosphere, 16
Thor-Able, 66, 67
Thor-Hustler, 77

Tikhov, G. A., 11
Transit, Project, 75-76
Troposphere, 16

Uranus, 11-12
USAF Aeromedical Laboratory, 32
Van Allen, Dr., James, 64
Vanguard, 63, 77
Vega, 78
Venus, 5, 10

Walker, Joseph A., 29-30
White, Alvin S., 29
White, Maj., Robert M., 29
Wolfe, Dr., John N., 20

X-15, 26, 75
X-2, 15

CLIVE E. DAVIS

started to build up his background in aviation in 1932, with an interest in glider flying. He soon turned to powered aircraft and served as aviation engineer with the Far East Air Force in World War II. Today, he holds a commercial pilot's license and is thoroughly familiar with both military and civilian airplanes. This was clearly indicated in his first book, THE JUNIOR AIRMAN'S BOOK OF AIRPLANES, a highly popular source of the very latest information for young air enthusiasts. Later he turned to missiles and rockets, handling them for an older audience with the same clear and concise treatment that is his special gift.

Born in the Unadilla River Valley, Chenango County, New York, at a place named Davis Crossing, after his grandfather, he attended Syracuse University's School of Journalism. For many years he has been associated with commercial broadcasting — radio, TV and motion picture writing, production and narration. He is currently employed by a California chain of radio and TV stations.

Clive Davis is married and has two sons, Doug and Bruce, who share his favorite hobby of anything connected with flying or airpower. In this, he is also enthusiastically supported by Mrs. Davis, who shares many of his flying experiences.